THE STUTTERER SPEAKS

The Stutterer Speaks

CONRAD F. WEDBERG

*Field Assistant, Bureau of Speech Correction, California
State Department of Education.
Director of Speech Therapy, Redlands City Schools*

VALLEY FINE ARTS PRESS

REDLANDS
CALIFORNIA

Printed by
THE CITROGRAPH PRINTING COMPANY
Redlands, California

DEDICATED

to

Alma, my loving wife, whose enduring faith and
encouragement inspired my victory,

and to

Mabel Farrington Gifford, who showed me the
way to emotional freedom and speech control.

FOREWORD

This is not a fairy tale. It is not an armchair fabrication written from hearsay, nor it is a sales book, artfully constructed to build up the stutterer's hopes and then leave him high and dry in the last chapter with a fervent plea to come here or go there and be cured. It is a message of encouragement, assuring the stutterer that he can do much for himself, inspired by my own life experiences and augmented by observations which I have made in dealing with many adult stutterers and with children in the public schools of Redlands, California.

Until I was thirty I stuttered, severely. For more than fifteen years I tried every suggestion, every conceivable cure to my knowledge, with always the same result, failure. When I finally came to the realization that my affliction was more than a mere speech defect, that it involved my whole personality, and that my stuttering was only the audible struggle of a greater battle going on within my emotional life, I attacked my problem from an entirely new approach. In exactly five weeks I emerged from the curse of a stutterer's existence and entered the realm of fluent and unhampered speech. Every word I have spoken since that glorious awakening, seven years ago, has been a real thrill, a source of inspiration that has led me to the writing of my story for the benefit of those who are still in the shackles of impeded speech.

I have no reason to believe that my case of stuttering was in any way unique, nor am I egotistical enough to think that my success was exceptional or beyond the reach of any one who desires sincerely enough the freedom which I have found. To live without the fear of imaginary inhibitions is a heavenly existence, available to any stutterer who conscientiously applies himself to his task, as I have outlined it in this book.

CONRAD F. WEDBERG

Redlands, California

CONTENTS

CHAPTER ONE

And Then They Laughed

I<small>T</small> W<small>AS</small> C<small>HRISTMAS</small> E<small>VE</small>. I remember that a cold wind was blowing and my teeth chattered as I rushed into the hardware store just before closing time. A group of clerks greeted me at the door-way. Gasping for breath, but smiling with eager anticipation, I proudly held out a shiny new silver dollar in the palm of my hand and tried to make known the object of my errand.

"I want a kn-n-n-", was as far as I got. The harder I tried the more severely I stuttered. I felt the blood rush to my cheeks as I turned away from the clerks to look into the nearest counter, hoping it contained pocketknives so that I could point to the gift which I wanted. I saw only eggbeaters and strainers, so I tried again to say the word "knife", but in vain. Suddenly the men broke out in lusty laughter. I looked at them and tried to smile, but something seemed to choke me. I knew then that it would be useless to try to talk again, so I turned and ran out of the store, trembling, afraid, not of the group of men, but of a new, strange feeling of weakness and embarrassment which I had never experienced before. I cried hysterically as I ran all of the way home, then sneaked upstairs, ashamed to face the kind uncle who had so brightened my spirits an hour before. I lay awake for many hours, clutching the silver dollar, wondering why this had happened to me, and dreading to face the next day without the gift I so longed for.

I was nine years old then and had been stuttering for more than two years, but until this incident occurred I had not become fully aware of the seriousness of my handicap. I knew of course that I did not talk like the rest of the boys, but this was the first experience in which my speech had failed me completely. Little did I imagine then that this was only the first of thousands of similar situations over which I would have no control.

As far as I have been able to learn I was born perfectly normal, physically and mentally, of normal parents. My early childhood days were spent on an orange ranch, in the companionship of three brothers and one sister. I was next to the oldest and the only one in the family who stuttered. From all appearances my home was a happy one and I should have been a happy child, but I was not. I was extremely sensitive, easily irritated, and generally dissatisfied with conditions that seemed quite satisfactory to the rest of the family. We had many friends and visitors who often remarked that ours was an ideal home. My parents held an enviable reputation in the church and I often took part in the Sunday school programs, singing and reciting jingles from the platform. This I really enjoyed, but how I dreaded the regular ordeal of reading a Bible verse in my class! Then I always stuttered and the boys, my best friends, always laughed at me.

My parents were Swedish. They came to this country only a short time before I was born, and naturally, could speak very little of our language. In fact, they learned most of their English from their children and continued to speak their native tongue in the home until I was about twelve years of age. This condition, where one language was spoken at home and another in the schoolroom, presented many difficult speech situations. The proper word at home was always the wrong word at school, and vice versa. For example, at home I was taught to say *poijk*. At school I learned that

this word meant *boy*. While endeavoring to find
the word which was apropos at the moment,
whether at home or at school, I stumbled and repeated the first letter, p-b-p-b, until my thoughts
associated the correct word with the situation.
This hesitation and repetition occurred on a number of other words, always causing the stumbling
on the first consonant, the bugaboo of all stutterers.

I mention this because, although it was not the
underlying cause of my stuttering, it probably did
fix my attention upon the first syllable of difficult
words. Many stutterers, if they can get past the
first syllable or the first word of a sentence, can
proceed without difficulty. Because many foreign
children in America stutter, we must consider this
confusion of two languages as an aggravating cause
when stuttering sets in soon after the foreign child
enters our schools.

Of vastly more importance than this language
difficulty was the economic situation in my home,
which had a direct bearing upon the attitudes and
feelings which I had about myself in relation to my
playmates. Our family was large and became
larger when we adopted an orphan cousin, while
my father had to provide for us with the meager
earnings of a laborer. We never suffered for want
of food or clothing, but it took considerable ingen-
uity on the part of my mother to provide six chil-

dren with homemade clothing from salvaged materials. In place of the popular baggy knickers, which were in vogue when I was in school, my trousers were skin tight and reached to approximately six inches above my knees. My shoes were half-soled by my father with thick, heavy leather which usually lasted a year. My knee-length stockings were almost as durable, homeknitted from heavy darning cotton. We wore long, black garters in those days, and you can imagine how artistically mine stretched from the bottom of my pants to the top of my stockings over six inches of contrasting white underwear! I dyed this visible patch of underwear with blue ink once—just once.

My hair was clipped every three months, sheared very closely in convict style, after it had grown long enough to hide my ears and collar completely. It amuses me now to recall how, after my hair had been twisted into braids by the boy who sat behind me in school, I would reappear the next day completely bald, a perfect target for stinging paper wads.

These peculiarities in dress prompted such nicknames as "Esau", "baldy", "clodhopper", and "tightbreeches". Of all of these, the last incensed me the most and provoked more fights than could possibly be good for a boy of my size and nervous temperament. It didn't help matters a bit when I asked my parents to dress me like my playmates always to receive the answer that there were thousands of little boys in Sweden who would be mighty happy to be as well-dressed as I. I knew that, as well as I knew that they had sleighs and ice skates in Sweden, but I had to play with California boys, and among them I was a misfit.

My older brother seemed to be quite satisfied with things as they were, but I, more sensitive and far more active, revolted against these conditions that did not seem to fit my scheme of life. I was always wishing that I could have things more like the other boys at school, be more like them, and be able to enjoy the freedom which they had. When I rebelled I was whipped, far too severely. If any good ever came out of the old-fashioned woodshed parties which my father held in my honor, I am sure that it would be measured in the emotional satisfaction which my father derived from them, not in the disciplinary results for which they were intended. Instead of developing obedience and respect these episodes only instilled in me, a sensitive and nervous child, attitudes of resentment and complete submission and feelings of helplessness which put me more and more on the defensive, increasing, naturally, the severity of my stuttering.

On the other hand, my parents sacrificed much for my welfare and always held before me the highest of ideals. We enjoyed a rare degree of family loyalty, a factor which I am sure made it easier for me to make adjustments to certain circumstances, in spite of my speech handicap.

I have no record of stuttering in the first grade. Reports indicate that I became a good reader in spite of my foreign accent, so if my stuttering had started it was probably not severe. In the second grade my teacher was quite provoked to find that I was writing with my left hand and immediately proceeded to teach me to write with my right hand. I was strictly left-handed in everything I did. I wrote with ease and quite legibly with my left hand and found it extremely difficult to change this habit, but my teacher insisted. She stood over me during writing periods, nagged and tormented me, and then punished me if I handed in papers which had been written with my left hand.*

I skipped the last half of the third grade and the first half of the fourth. My memories of this period are too hazy to recall with accuracy, as far as speaking experiences are concerned. When I en-

*(This interference with the preferred hand is considered by some neurologists in the field of speech pathology to be the direct cause of stuttering. The emotional disturbance caused by this forced change in handedness was in my case, as in the case of a few others with whom I have worked, like the confusion of two languages, an aggravating factor. But stuttering is not caused by the changes which are supposed to take place in the nervous system and the brain when a left-handed child learns to write with his right hand. See chapter three.)

tered the fifth grade, one full year ahead of schedule, I found myself smaller and younger than any
of my classmates. My experiences in this grade
stand out above all other memories of my school
life. It was here that I first became extremely self-
conscious about my impediment. Every day I was
reminded in one way or another that I was different, that there was something wrong with me —
that I could not talk. The boys made an ugly duckling of me on the playground and would not let me
play with them because I was too small and because I stuttered badly in the excitement of games;
yet they mocked me and teased me for playing
with boys in the lower grades. I could have licked
many of them singly, for I was clever with my left
hand, but they usually turned it into a ten-to-one
melee and then blamed me for starting the fight.

My teacher in the fifth grade was very irritable
and impatient, particularly with me. She demanded strict discipline and exacted it with a high-
pitched, raspy voice. Her attitude toward my
speech impediment was anything but sympathetic.
Although she insisted upon my taking part in recitations, the amusement which my efforts provoked
from my classmates embarrassed me so painfully
that I soon refused to recite. I usually knew the
answers, but I had such a fear of reciting that I
tried every scheme I could think of to avoid the or-

deal. I remember slipping down behind my desk in the hope that I would not be seen and called upon. On one occasion I faked a nosebleed the moment before it was my turn to recite and started for the washroom, but I was caught in the subterfuge and was severely punished.

Occasionally I would gather enough courage to volunteer, only to hear the tittering of my classmates as soon as I stumbled on a difficult word, so I would sit down before I had finished the recitation. My teacher insisted that if I only knew my lesson I could stand up and recite without stuttering. She frequently scolded me before the class for my failure and then kept me after school to study the lesson which I could say almost from memory, but not one word of which I could repeat in a classroom recitation.

Once I was sent to the principal's office, a sanctum reserved for bad boys. I feared this principal like a mystic god, for when boys were sent to her office for a whipping they never returned to the classroom until the following day. I had failed to hear the silence bell on the playground, or had committed some such serious offense, and it was my teacher who sent me to the office. I was crying long before I reached the switching post, but the principal surprised me by taking me immediately into her confidence. She explained that my teacher thought that I was dumb and lazy, but that I really was not. "You are stubborn and antagonistic", she said, "and should try harder to do what you are told."

Try? God knows how hard I tried, how I wanted to measure up and do my part! My heart cried out for a little understanding, for some way of escape from that tantalizing feeling of helplessness, and against the unbearable domination of that teacher. And then she held me back an extra half-year in her grade because I was dumb!

CHAPTER TWO

Stumbling Along

My hopes brightened during the next year as a great change took place in my school life. My sixth grade teacher, quite young and attractive, was admired and respected by all of the class. She was patient, calm and composed, and always cheerful in her work. She never pointed out failures in front of the class, and she handled discipline successfully with kindness. As soon as she learned that I stuttered she called me to her desk and suggested that I do most of my work in writing and that I read to her alone at noon or after school. One day I was sent out of the room on an errand. While I was gone my teacher explained my difficulty to the class and asked them to always sympa-

23

thize and never ridicule my efforts. She told them, according to my brother who was in the room, that I was one of the smartest boys in the room but was afraid to speak because they laughed. Unaware of this, I courageously volunteered one day to recite. Although I stuttered quite badly there was no snickering and my efforts were commented upon with exaggerated encouragement!

Before the year was over I was reciting in turn, reading and talking continuously, with very little stuttering. I got good grades in my work, became cheerful and happy, and made friends with many of my former enemies. I was invited to join in the playground games and was no longer treated as an ugly duckling. I was able to earn a little spending money after school, every cent of which I spent on store clothes and barber shop hair-cuts. Life presented a much brighter picture than it ever had before, in the schoolroom, on the playground, and at home.

This interim of improved speech continued through my four years in high school. At times I did stutter quite severely, but it did not worry me for most of the time I spoke with very little hesitation. In my junior year I was elected tennis captain and occasionally made short speeches before the entire student body. Some of my classmates joked about my impediment, but I only laughed with them, feeling certain now that it would soon be outgrown.

This, however, was not to be my good fortune. Because I had not expected to go on to college I had taken mostly mechanical and business courses in high school. I found that in order to become a freshman in the college of my home town, it would be necessary for me to go one whole year making up entrance requirements in English, history, languages, and mathematics. In all of these classes I was required to take part in oral recitations, and it was not long until the old fear and dread of my fifth grade experiences returned. My stuttering became decidedly worse. I avoided companionships, for which I was considered haughty and conceited; I became moody and sensitive again and unfriendly, and I worried day and night about my predicament.

The thing that discouraged me most of all was the realization that I could no longer detour around a difficult bugaboo word with the substitution of a clever synonym, a ruse which I had developed very successfully in high school. In college I had to be explicit. Much of my study time was spent in searching for synonyms which might be used in place of words that began with hard, explosive consonants. I never found a synonym for the word *trapezoid*, much to my humiliation. I remember standing before a class in mathematics, trying to explain something about a lopsided figure on the blackboard. It wasn't a parallelogram or a trapezium—words which I could say because the accent did not fall upon the first syllable—but for this professor it had to be called a trapezoid. I got as far as the word trapezoid in my explanation when my tongue froze to the roof of my mouth. Some kind student in the front row relieved me by saying the word. "Yes", I agreed, "this t-t-t-" and again my tongue stuck, tighter than ever, to my palate. One of the campus wits called me "trape-zoid" that afternoon and I carried the name for many weeks. Every time I heard the word my conscience burned with self-reproach and made me wish that I had never attempted college. I developed a keen word-consciousness that doubled the severity of my affliction.

I was happy when the World War offered an opportunity during my sophomore year to get away from it all. I could be a hero for a time at least without having to talk. Here again psychology came to my rescue. Regular hours of sleep, regular meals, and healthy exercise built me up physically. I became less nervous and my speech improved rapidly. Confidence returned when I was placed in the first squad with the tallest men of my company and was given the pivot position in the drills. One day I took my turn in the capacity of commanding officer. I shouted my commands vigorously and drilled the company with perfect success. This experience prompted me to apply immediately for transference to an officers' training camp. I studied diligently, developing daily a new command of myself and an unusual degree of poise. I was certain this time that I had at last completely conquered the stuttering devil.

Four days before the armistice was signed I was called in to take an oral examination before a group of commanding officers. I remember smiling at the major with a debonair attitude of self-confidence, though inwardly I was quite nervous and my heart was pounding furiously. In my excitement I forgot to salute the officers. The first question, instead of the one which I was prepared to answer, was "Why did you not salute your commanding officer?"

I do not remember much of what happened after that. I tried to make a feeble explanation, but I was stumped! I couldn't utter a word. I did not wait to be excused, but turned on my heel, made a halfway salute, and walked out of the barracks with my head down. I had never suffered such a feeling of disgust and self-pity, and I am not ashamed to admit that I cried like a child. That evening my captain came to me and told me that he was sorry, that he hoped I would do better next time. Pity? I didn't want pity! I wanted to know why this damnable curse had to overwhelm me every time I had an even chance for advancement! Why, when I wanted to do my best, the harder I tried the worse my affliction became! I didn't want another chance—I knew that I would fail. My hopes of ever correcting my stuttering vanished completely. Again I was slave, stuttering my master.

The next five years I spent on a large ranch in northern California, isolated from the requirements of social communication. I worked hard, seven days a week, spending most of my time alone, worrying, cursing my fate, knowing that I had the mental ability to perform tasks far above the level of menial labor at which I was employed. Minor promotions and raises in wages only taunted me, for I knew that I would get only so far and then be faced again with the inability to meet situations where speech would be required. The event that perhaps saved me from complete mental breakdown was the organization of a home talent orchestra on the ranch. I played a banjo sufficiently well to get a steady job playing for country dances once a week. I sang the refrains of popular songs through a large megaphone, and although I was no meadow lark, I managed to hold the job in spite of better banjo players.

In nineteen twenty-two I was promoted to the position of subforeman on the ranch and was married the following year. My experiences from that time until I corrected my stuttering, eight years later, would be only a repetition of much that has been said. I had moments of hopefulness when my speech seemed to be improving, but inevitably I returned, sooner or later, to the painful existence of a confirmed stutterer.

After a prolonged siege of typhoid fever, which kept me confined for seven months, my stuttering became decidedly worse. I was finally requested to resign from my administrative position unless I could do something about my speech. I fully realized that this request was justified, for the men under my supervision no longer respected my authority, but nevertheless I reacted with indignation and resigned immediately. I moved my family to my home town in southern California and went to work as a day laborer on a large orange ranch. My wife, who had been a school teacher, found a job and began teaching again to help support the family. By this time my self-confidence and self-respect were almost completely gone, and when my two boys began to imitate me in their speech I became more than ever convinced that I was a complete failure.

I turned to smoking excessively and drinking occasionally, but found no solace there. I searched the shelves of libraries for books about stuttering but none of them told me *why* I stuttered or what to do about it. In one I read that my type of stuttering was not severe, not as severe as some types, for mine was merely a case of pneumo-laryngo-gnathocheilomania! Perhaps this revelation should have cheered me up, but inwardly I felt that I was in distress enough without anything like that happening to me. Other books expounded the theory that stutterers lack rhythm. I was full of it! I had always been musical, I had good muscle coordination in athletics, and I danced well. I decided that these books were written by charlatans, for they invariably contained a chapter entitled, "The Cure", which was nothing more than an urgent invitation to attend such and such an institution for expensive but immediate relief.

The last three years of my life as a stutterer come back to me now as a living nightmare. I suffered from chronic headaches, nervous indigestion, and many other ills which caused me to excuse myself from social obligations which I could have and should have met but did not want to face because of my neurotic state of mind. A peculiar change came over me, a craving for excitement, a mania for driving my car at dangerously high speeds, in spite of the discomfort it caused my family, and the habit of living in a constant state of nervous tension from which I seldom relaxed, even at night. I can hardly describe the sensations that came over me when I would awaken in the night, trembling, as alert and wide awake as when I went to bed, tense with fear of something, I knew not what. I obtained my only relief in going to the radio and searching for foreign stations until sheer exhaustion drove me back to sleep. On days following such spells of insomnia I found it practically impossible to say a word without blocking completely.

I finally fell a victim to claustrophobia, the terrorizing fear of strangling in dark or closed places. Many times I climbed ten flights of stairs to avoid thirty seconds in an elevator, and often I ran from a closed room or a dark theater to get a full breath of fresh air. Once I almost fainted when traffic held up my car for less than a minute in a dark tunnel.

While these changes were taking place in my mental and emotional life, the spasms and contortions of stuttering, which had formerly been confined to my speech organs, diffused to all parts of my body. When I tried to speak my whole body trembled. I would feel weak and faint and some-

times I could scarcely see or hear, my mind imper-
vious to everything about me except my own efforts to force out a difficult word for which I could
find no synonym.

It was in this condition of almost complete
physical, mental, and emotional breakdown, in
which I feared to face another night of sleepless-
ness and another day of anxiety, that my wife
found me one gloomy winter evening, seven years
ago. She asked me to go with her to hear a lecture
about the correction of stuttering and stammering
in the schools. My first reaction was an indignant
"No!", but when she explained that all teachers
were required to go and that she needed an escort,
I condescended. The lecturer was Mrs. Mabel
Farrington Gifford, chief of the speech correction
department of the state of California.

I listened to her first remarks with doubt and
skepticism. What did she know about it, I wondered. I was impressed, however, with her poise
and self-assurance, her beautiful diction, and her
voice. Then someone whispered that she had once
stuttered herself, had studied abroad with prominent psychiatrists, had corrected her own impediment, and had cured hundreds of children in the
schools and many adults. I began to listen then,
attentively, and before long I felt that she was re-
lating my own case history, for her remarks fol-

lowed very closely my own experiences of the past. She told us *why* children stuttered, *why* the habit persisted into adulthood, and *why* it could not be shaken loose without a new, psychological understanding of the problem. Her statements were convincing. Her personality demanded admiration. Her voice inspired emulation.

I left the auditorium that night with a new interpretation of my affliction and a new hope, a vision that has become reality.

vv

CHAPTER THREE

Facing the Facts

THIS STORY OF MY STUTTERING experiences and
the procedure which I followed in reestablishing
fluent speech is written with the knowledge that
there are almost a million individuals in the United
States afflicted with some type of nervous speech
disorder. The majority of these are persons who
will have to do what they can about their stuttering themselves, without outside assistance, or do
nothing at all. It is to them, primarily, that I am
writing this message of encouragement. Psychological clinics and trained experts in speech correction are available in only a few of our larger cities.
Modern, scientific treatises on stuttering which appear in professional speech journals or between the

covers of expensive books seldom reach the layman, the confirmed stutterer of community life, who, with the right understanding of his problem, can do much for himself.

Most stutterers have become wise enough to turn a deaf ear to the pleas of quacks and charlatans who have been permitted to exploit stutterers, ruthlessly, for financial gain. Fewer stutterers are being victimized by scare letters and guarantees of cure offered by our so-called stammering institutions. No one can guarantee a permanent cure for stuttering or any other nervous speech disorder, and certainly not those who employ the swinging of dumb-bells and singsong speech drills as a means of eliminating the symptoms of stuttering without considering the cause or the motivation behind it.

What can the stutterer do for himself? Must he spend hundreds of dollars and years of time with a psychoanalyst? Can he be cured by someone else? Will he eventually outgrow the impediment, will it miraculously disappear, or must the chronic stutterer continue to grope about for some new trick or device that will only temporarily relieve the struggle? These and other questions in the mind of the habitual stutterer should be answered, and he should be given a new psychological understanding of his problem before the second part of my personal story is presented.

The facts of the case are not so discouraging as they might have appeared to the stutterer who has been the victim of countless faulty suggestions and well meant but fallacious bits of advice. "Take a deep breath", "slow down", "drawl your words", or "think what you are going to say" are the most common of these, impossible to put into practice when the stutterer is caught in the throes of physical tension and emotional strain. Failure only causes more discouragement, more emotional disturbance, and in turn more severe stuttering. Let us first, by the process of elimination, cast aside some of the distracting ideas which the average stutterer has adopted regarding his affliction.

The stutterer must get out of his mind the idea that he can be "cured" by someone else. His malady involves no physiological or congenital defects for which a cure can be prescribed. In fact, there is nothing to be cured! Normal speech is there, as it ever has been, ready to be used as soon as emotional interference and psychic inhibitions are removed. The stutterer cannot transfer to another person the burden of removing his impediment, as a patient surrenders himself to a physician for a major operation, no matter how competent the speech therapist may be, for the stutterer suggested himself into his predicament and he, himself, must find his way out. He must go back to the begin-

ning of his speech troubles, begin all over again
with new ideas about speech and social adjustments, and through the application of these in
speaking situations he must establish new physical,
mental, and emotional habits. The competent
psychotherapist can help the stutterer to understand his problem and guide him in his psychological readjustments, but whatever is done to actually
overcome the stuttering is done by the individual
himself. Emotional control and constructive thinking must be practiced in those social situations
where anxiety and tension have prevailed, and this
cannot be done by proxy. My first advice to an
adult patient is always, "You will do this yourself
—I cannot do it for you."

We must be concerned with the cause of stuttering in each individual case, the conditions under
which inhibited speech first began. Failure to consider these factors accounts for the hopelessness of
various cures in the past. Ever since Demosthenes
juggled a few pebbles in his mouth and shouted his
orations to the waves, three hundred and eighty-
five years before Christ, master minds have been
baffled by the symptoms of this strange and complex malady. Tongues have been slit, tonsils and
uvulas have been removed, and numberless speech
drills have been tried in the past. Even today
expensive laboratories are equipped to test the stut-

terer's heart beat and respiration count, fitting pro-
cedures for research purposes, but of little value in
the treatment or correction of the affliction. Present day methods of treatment which are based upon the erroneous supposition that in stuttering the
speech organs fail to function properly because of
some pathological condition in the muscles and
nerves involved, are doomed to failure, for dealing
with symptoms will not remove causes!

We know that in stuttering there is nothing or-
ganically wrong with the organs of speech. Under
certain favorable conditions every stutterer can
speak without a sign of hesitation. This would be
impossible if any physiological defect existed.
There are preachers who are eloquent in the pulpit
but who cannot speak a complete sentence in conversation with their parishioners without stuttering. A prominent lawyer of my acquaintance
memorizes long passages from his law books, for as
long as they appear to be his own expression he or-
ates with perfect fluency. He cannot read a word
from the book without stuttering. Some stutterers
are able to swear with rare ability, while others
cannot make an audible sound when angry. In my
own case, my saddle horse never heard me stutter
on a single word of the lengthy, one-sided conversations which I carried on with him about the day's
work ahead; but just as soon as another person

entered the situation, and particularly when that person was my employer, my saddle horse must have wondered if another rider had mysteriously slipped into the saddle. Anger usually closed my jaws like a vise, and at the telephone I was practically speechless.

We need not be concerned with the various ways in which stuttering manifests itself in different individuals, nor by its irregularity of appearance in the same individual. The various types of hesitancy, prolonged repetitions, facial contortions, or muscular spasms of the speech organs, indicate nothing regarding the basic origin of the disorder or the procedure for correction. In other words, it is not the kind of speech defect with which we are concerned, but rather the kind of person who has the speech defect. Whatever form the stutter may take, whether the struggle resolves itself into spasmodic blocking, silent stammering, cluttering, or rapid repetition of one letter or syllable, the vital point of attack is the same, the maladjusted personality endeavoring to function behind the stuttering. Because it appears only in social situations, in the presence of other persons—practically every stutterer can speak when alone—it is the social being who is in distress, floundering, struggling, failing to function normally because of something *inside* over which he seemingly has no control.

Much has been said about left-handedness, or more explicitly, the changing from left to right-handedness, as the cause of stuttering. Only recently one of my patients, whom I called upon at the request of interested friends, said defiantly that nothing could be done for him because he was left-handed. "I have been told", he said, "that there is a confusion in my brain because I use my left hand, and that I must become totally right-handed before I can get over my stuttering. I can't do that because my work demands the use of my left hand." This young man had completely surrendered himself to stuttering for the rest of his life because he believed that his brain would not permit him to be left-handed and talk at the same time. Incidentally, he has made rapid improvement with a new psychological approach to his problem.

Briefly, the explanation of the cerebral dominance theory, which links left-handedness with stuttering, is as follows: The left side of the brain controls the right side of the body, and the right side of the brain controls the left side of the body. The area of the brain which controls speech is supposed to be located in one-half of the brain, in that half which controls the dominant side of the body. If a person is left-handed, then, the speech area should be in the right half of the brain. This half of the brain is called the dominant sector because it controls the dominant side of the body, and this dominance, it is held, must not be interfered with. Therefore, if a child is left-handed and is forced to write with his right hand he must use the left side of the brain which is not dominant, and which does not have control of speech. Writing is considered to be a form of speech, so when a left-handed child writes with his right hand a disturbance in brain dominance or a conflict between the two halves of the brain results, causing stuttering.

A few observations should clear up any misunderstanding about this neurological theory. In the first place, the assumption that speech is in any way related to handedness is only guesswork, for the cerebral dominance theory, upon which all of the above conclusions are based, has never been scientifically proved. When it was common practice in our schools to teach a left-handed child to write with his right hand, it was observed that in some cases the child began to stutter soon after the change was made. This discovery led to much experimentation, most of which has been conducted by Dr. Lee Edward Travis at the University of Iowa, in an effort to prove that all cases of stuttering (and stammering) are caused by interference with preferential handedness.

When this subject came up for discussion in a psychology course at the University of California,

the late Dr. Sheppard I. Franz, eminent psychologist and brain specialist, made these statements:

"It is not abnormal to be left-handed. There are
all degrees of ambidexterity in different individuals,
and whether we are more right-handed or more
left-handed we continually use both sides of the
brain to direct the motor body. Writing is a com-
paratively late accomplishment, coming long after
talking has been learned. The brain should be sufficiently practiced in controlling speech to overcome any changes attempted in writing. However,
it is natural for a child to write with the dominant
hand. To try to teach a left-handed child to do
awkwardly with his right hand a task which he can
perform with ease and satisfaction with his left
hand is bound to cause discouragement and emotional strain. This in itself, although no actual
nerve derangements take place in the brain, is sufficient to cause stuttering in sensitive, nervous children. By all means permit a child to write with the
hand which he has voluntarily chosen!"

It is not definitely known what lies behind man-
ual preference, but the most accepted theory at the
present time indicates that prenatal conditions
have much to do with it. If during the period
when the nerves of the hands and arms are being
formed the embryo is in such a position that the
left hand is permitted more freedom than the right

43.

---

hand, the left hand is likely to become more dexterous and be given preference after birth. Interference with this preference, particularly when accompanied with nagging and fussing of over-exacting teachers and parents, is certain to cause nervous tension and emotional disturbance and have other psychological effects which are known to cause permanent speech disorders.

My own case is typical of so-called neurological derangement. I was decidedly left-handed and was forced to learn to write with my right hand. I continue to write, turn the pages of a book, carry a suitcase, open doors, and do many other things with my right hand; I play golf and tennis, chop wood, and do all heavy work with my left hand. I was made to feel quite inferior about my left-handedness, so I made every possible effort to become totally right-handed in everything I did. Today the left-handed boy is encouraged to become another "Lefty" Grove, of baseball fame, a fortunate reversal in attitude toward a perfectly normal condition.

Finally, if the act of stuttering involves definite neuro-muscular alterations in the nerves of the brain and in the organs used in speech, it would appear that a stutterer's thoughts, feelings, and emotions should have no bearing upon his difficulty. It would follow then that he would stutter consistently in all life situations. This we know is not the

case. I was just as left-handed when I talked with
ease to my dog or saddle horse as I was when I
stood speechless before the army officers. More-
over, we must account for stuttering in those who
are congenitally right-handed, a condition which
according to statistics prevails in the majority of
cases.

Some stutterers have been led to believe that,
because their affliction is classified by some psychologists as a neurosis, it is a type of insanity, curable
only by the expensive and tedious process of psychoanalysis. It should be known that the results
from the psychoanalytical treatment of stuttering
have been far from gratifying, if not disappointing.
Perhaps, in a few isolated cases, when stuttering is
accompanied by the symptoms of a psychosis or
other definite mental illness, intensive and prolonged exploration of the unconscious mind is necessary. But stuttering in general does not fall under the classification of mental derangements
which lead to nervous breakdown or insanity.

The purpose of psychoanalysis, briefly, is to uncover submerged complexes in the unconscious
mind which date back to unfortunate experiences
in childhood. These experiences are completely forgotten, consciously, because of their unpleasantness, but instead of being pushed completely out of
the mind they are repressed into the unconscious

reservoir of memory. In later years they return to the surface in disguised forms such as phobias, delusions, obsessions, and compulsions, and completely overrule all conscious efforts of the victim to control himself. Because these repressions are not recognized and cannot be recalled by the conscious mind, the psychoanalyst uncovers them by processes of unconscious thinking—word associations, hypnotism, dream analysis, or automatic writing — and brings them into consciousness where they are understood and gradually drained off.

It is true that stuttering is caused by emotional conflicts growing out of distressing experiences in childhood, but there is one important distinction between the stutterer's mental life and that of the psychopathic personality who requires psychoanalytical treatment. In the case of the latter the conflict is bottled up, so to speak, and is not permitted to enter the conscious realm of thought. The dread of stuttering, on the other hand, is present in both the conscious and the unconscious. The very act of stuttering serves as an outlet or a conscious expression for the emotional conflict underneath which is causing the speech disturbance. Finding a way out in conscious activity, although tormenting to the stutterer, is actually a relief for the conflict which might otherwise have become a far more serious affliction.

This is a very important point in the interpretation of the stutterer's problem, for it makes possible the procedure of self-analysis and personality rehabilitation by the stutterer himself. The stutterer knows that while he is endeavoring to talk he is consciously aware of far more than the struggle which is taking place in his organs of speech. His feelings, emotional states, and nervous sensations, which vary in intensity with each speaking situation, are constant reminders of like situations that have occurred before. Through these conscious experiences, by reflecting upon attitudes, ideas, and sentiments which have evolved about earlier stuttering situations, the stutterer himself is able to trace back through his past, as would the analyst by the devious paths of unconscious thinking, to the emotional atmosphere of that period when stuttering first began.

This procedure suggested itself to me when I was left alone with my own problem. It worked so perfectly in the eradication of my fear of closed places and in giving me an understanding of my faulty emotional reactions to the social group as a child, that I submit it, without any apologies to the field of psychoanalysis, as a helpful step towards speech freedom. To avoid confusion we shall coin a new word, *auto-analysis,* for this procedure.

The stutterer's problem is threefold. First he must return by the process of auto-analysis to the period of childhood in which stuttering first began and survey the conditions and the atmosphere that surrounded him and influenced his emotional life at that time. Although it will probably be impossible to recall the specific incident—if there was one— that caused the first speech blocking, the general emotional atmosphere in which the stuttering arose can be revived. Then with adult judgment the stutterer must interpret these influences, rationally, with reason and understanding, and dismiss them as childish impressions which guided him in his reactions to society before a sense of reasoning power had been developed.

Second, the stutterer must take inventory of his present attitudes and feelings, some of which have developed as a result of stuttering, and, considering his whole personality as the product of a psychological life badly warped by emotional disturbances which need continue no longer, he must reconstruct new patterns of emotional living and a new personality of composure and self-confidence.

Third, the stutterer must convince himself by actually doing so that he *can* speak without stuttering. This he can do without tension and strain, effortlessly, when the emotional anxiety which has upset him in speaking situations is absent.

Such a program involves many phases of human behavior, particularly child behavior, which the majority of stutterers have never considered to be responsible for their affliction. Emotional states, instinctive urges, the ways of the mind, both conscious and unconscious, and habit formation, each play an important role in the cause and correction of stuttering. Each individual must become familiar with the way these functions have worked against each other in his own life to bring about the maladjusted personality that is now his major problem. It is an interesting course of procedure, I can assure you, and the only one that will serve to remove all of the complications of the stutterer's problem.

CHAPTER FOUR

Emotional Sham Battles

It has been very aptly said that the stutterer is a person who is not *on* his way, but rather, *in* his way. Certainly this is true. Instead of moving forward, facing life offensively, he is psychologically on the defensive. The nervous tension and physical effort which he exhibits in speaking situations is an entirely unnecessary waste of energy, as far as overcoming any obstacle between himself and his auditors is concerned, for society is practically always on his side. People who listen to the stutterer would do anything they could to help him along, and the stutterer knows this; yet, even before attempting to speak, the stutterer feels "cornered", as if he were challenged and could not

49

measure up, and the harder he consciously tries not to stutter the more severe the spasms become. The audible struggle which takes place in the organs of speech is merely an outward manifestation of a greater battle going on within the social self, a use-less battle between emotional forces that refuse to work together in harmony.

If we were to make any one definite distinction between normal speech and stuttering, aside from symptomatic impressions, we would say that nor-mal speech is an automatic, unconsciously directed process, while almost every word spoken by the stutterer requires a conscious effort. The normal speaker pays no more conscious attention to the production of speech sounds than he does to the functions of breathing or walking. The stutterer, on the other hand, particularly one who has strug-gled with his impediment for many years, weighs his words cautiously, thinks about difficult sounds before he comes to them, and endeavors con-sciously to control the muscles and nerves involved in talking. Instead of assisting himself he actually causes interference with a function that should long since have been relegated to involuntary con-trol. This matter of conscious interference follows a common psychological law, that we cannot con-sciously improve upon a performance that has been taken over by the habit regions of the brain. A good example of this is in the application of the footbrakes of an automobile. In case of a sudden emergency the foot strikes the brake pedal in a split second, accurately, far more accurately than if the driver tried to consciously place it there.

It is not difficult to understand why the stutterer should direct his conscious effort upon talking when every speech situation is anticipated with a certain degree of fear, expectation of failure, or dread of humiliation. Anxiety is always present in the stutterer's mind, some of which is, naturally, well-founded upon memories of countless aggravating experiences in the past. But a large part of this anxiety, involving nervousness, feelings of inferiority and helplessness, the attitude of being on the defensive, and the feeling of insecurity in the presence of others, is not attributable to stuttering experiences at all. It is the rapidly expanding growth of an original nucleus of anxiety that already existed in the child mind when the stuttering first began. Something went amiss, frustration of some sort interfered with the child's efforts to adjust himself to persons and conditions in his early environment, and, whatever it was that upset his emotional equilibrium, it interfered with the slowly developing habits of speech and brought them into conscious attention.

Approaching the problem then from this angle,

each individual must thoroughly survey the early environment in which his own emotional conflicts were aroused. There are so many causes for emotional disturbance in the lives of children, as they are forced to restrict and control their activities to conform with our modern, mostly urban regime of living, that it is usually quite easy to trace back to something, either exciting or depressing, that seared deeply and left an indelible mark upon the early emotional patterns of childhood behavior.

Let us look into a modern home for a moment and get better acquainted with emotions. Mrs. Jones is busy in her kitchen, too busy to keep a watchful eye on little Bobby, four years old. Bobby's exploring instinct has led him to the sink, where he has climbed upon a stool to gain a better view of those many strange looking utensils. His curiosity urges him to examine a long, sharp, butcher knife, one which he has seen many times before in the hands of his father. He picks it up, flourishes it with sweeping satisfaction toward his mother, and says to the best of his ability, "Knipe!" His ecstasy is suddenly broken by a terrifying scream. His eyes open wide with fear. The knife is jerked roughly from his grasp and his hands are severely slapped. Bobby looks into his mother's face and is frightened by the strange look of terror in her eyes. Tears suddenly blind him as he looks about for protection. The sharp, loud tones of his mother's voice, expressing fear, bewilder him. Then he is roughly pushed into another room and the door is slammed behind him, separating him from the apron strings which mean security and confidence to him, and which he needs now more than at any other time in his life.

What has happened? Agree with me that nothing has happened to his organs of speech. First of all his natural impulse of curiosity was thwarted. Next his urge for acquisition, a fundamental, inborn desire, was frustrated. Then, with the scream of terror and the slapping of his hands, mixed emotions of fear and anger were aroused. Immediate flight from the situation was inhibited by his feelings of helplessness. Wonder, anxiety, doubt, and submission likely followed in rapid order, and then loneliness, isolation from the one whom he had always depended upon to protect him and provide for him. As Bobby huddled near the door and cried it out, reviewing in his mind the unpleasant details of the episode, his emotions continually changed from one state to another.

A few weeks later this little boy—whose name, for obvious reasons, is not Bobby Jones — was brought by his mother to one of my school clinics. He stuttered, badly. His mother was not only worried; she was provoked, principally because the boy had become sulky and stubborn in his attitude toward her. He seldom stuttered when talking with his father, she said, but almost constantly with her, especially when excited and when he wanted to ask for something. The mother's account of the case was typical, almost amusing to me as she betrayed —but avoided any reference to—her own high-strung disposition. Bobby was not left-handed, he had experienced no accidents or severe shocks, he was not sickly, and as far as the mother knew he had never been frightened!

Our discussion of emotions finally brought out the knife episode, my questions leading to the details which I have related. She left me with the assurance that she would do something about her own temperament and establish a new atmosphere of serenity and security for the child in his home. In less than a month she reported that the stutter had entirely disappeared.

It is not difficult to see how the word "knipe" would be associated with this unforgettable emotional experience, and how the handling of this or any other knife would bring into consciousness the memory of the various distressing aspects of this episode. If Bobby were to ask for the knife again, or happened to be caught playing with it, undoubtedly his attempt to name it would result in "kn-n-nnipe", or some other manifestation of inhibited speech.

The association of emotional tone with speaking situations is inevitable, because there exists an unbreakable bond between emotions and speech. Every dominant emotion expresses itself in one way or another through the voice. Curiosity is indicated by a rising inflection; anger by sharp, loud tones; sorrow by milder, lower tones; and fear, depending upon its intensity, by either high-pitched screams or complete blocking of all utterance. Can you imagine a person offering condolences in shouting, or two persons carrying on a heated quarrel in whispers? Even the infant in his crib makes it clear by the tone and intensity of a baby cry what it would say if it could, whether it is sleepy or hungry, or whether it has gas pains or is being stuck by a towel pin.

The voice is literally the mouthpiece of the emotions, the transmitter of feelings, attitudes, and opinions. It is our most universal means of communication, the means through which we exchange ideas, likes and dislikes, fears and hopes, and betray —unless we are wary—our inner secrets of guilt or pride. All of these are in some degree emotional expressions. If emotional conflict is going on within, the expression of it will be conflict in speech, as we find in stuttering. It is chiefly through the

medium of speech that social relationships are established; and we are, above all else, by nature gre-
garious, social beings, constantly striving to measure up to social requirements and to be accepted as
a unit of one group or another of society. It is
only when emotional conflict, flavored with anxiety and dread, becomes associated with speech
that we place undue emphasis upon the performance of the organs which produce it, as in the case
of stuttering.

The causes of emotional conflicts are legion.
The most common is the adjustment which every
child is forced to make when his natural impulses
—otherwise called primitive urges, instinctive
drives, or racially inherited traits—are suppressed
by modern conventions, taboos, and adult ideals of
behavior. The child of today is born into a social
environment in which he is inherently a total
stranger. He is endowed, as was primitive man
centuries ago, with animal instincts that fit him for
survival and self-expression in a world of simple life
far different from the social regime to which he
must adjust himself today.

The unlearned pattern of primitive behavior
with which the human child is provided would
guide him to preserve himself by seeking food and
shelter, to protect himself, to satisfy his curiosity,
to flee from danger, to combat and overcome obsta-

cles, and later, to procreate his kind. The purpose of these inborn traits is for the body to function, develop, and survive. Fulfillment of them creates a state of satisfaction; restrictions that interfere with their completion cause annoyance, and, in some children, extreme emotional confusion.

Note that this instinctive pattern of behavior does not include manners, talking, submission to parental authority or domination by others, postponement of satisfaction and pleasure, conformity to rules and regulations, thoughtfulness of others, or cleanliness. The human child is indifferent toward dirt. He is really much in favor of it, more so than the common house cat, which is always licking it away. The wearing of clothing and keeping it clean is not incorporated in the primitive child's code of living, and this may often be the cause of serious conflict, especially when a tired mother bombards her child in a high-pitched voice with complaints about extra washing.

Nor is talking a biological inheritance of the human race. Nature did not provide us with a special mechanism for speech as it did for sight and hearing. Speech is a learned function, perhaps the most highly specialized of man's accomplishments, for its production requires the borrowing and coordinating of various muscles and nerves that were primarily intended for other specific duties. It takes many years for a child to train these organs, which he naturally uses for the grosser functions of breathing, chewing, and swallowing, to make the delicate adjustments required for the formation of the intricate sounds of modern language. And fortunate is the child who gets through this period without some emotional stress. Parents too frequently drive the child into submission and timidity by trying to make him perform beyond his ability in speech development.

Thwarting of the sex drive is another cause for emotional conflict, although in my opinion this phase of adjustment is greatly over-emphasized in its bearing upon stuttering. Some psychiatrists contend that all conflict is based upon sex and the love life, a contention that is difficult to accept when we think of the broader scope of childhood emotions. It is not natural for boys and girls to postpone mating and withhold the expression of sex desires as modern conventions decree, but the suppression of this urge is not usually encountered until approaching adolescence, long after the majority of cases of stuttering have developed.

However, related to the sex problem is one common practice among parents that is very frequently the cause of serious conflict. The human child is by nature an inquisitive creature, constantly aroused by curiosity to explore new things; at the same time he is decidedly an exhibitionist. During that early period of childhood when these impulses are limited to the exploration of his own body, it is only natural for the child to discover and become interested in the parts of his body which are by modern convention shrouded with secrecy and taboo. The child sees no rhyme or reason for this. The discoveries which he makes provide him with a great amount of satisfaction; his next impulse is to enjoy and exhibit his findings as he did when he first discovered his toes as a part of him. These explorations and gratifying revelations, by which the child establishes his own identity and self-importance, are accompanied by favorable responses. But when parents who have forgotten their own childhood, who have become strict believers in some of the veiled superstitions of sex, interfere, with emotional outbursts of disapproval and restraint, gratification usually changes to fear and secrecy.

These situations could be handled with discretion and judgment so as to leave no disturbing emotional memories in the mind of the child, but unfortunately a scene is usually created, followed by a vigil of fear, stupid warnings, and often threats. Caution and over-anxiety about the habit of masturbation, which so many parents dread, is not only untimely in most cases, but is almost certain to lay the foundation for unhealthy attitudes toward sex impulses when they do come to life and adjustments must be made to control them.

It is pertinent here to note that on the islands of the South Seas, where savages live in a primitive way and encourage the full expression of their racial instincts, mental illness and nervous speech disorders are practically unknown.

The conclusion which we must reach is that during the speech developing period, while the child is inclined to be guided in his behavior by racially inherited instincts, and before he has developed sufficient reasoning power to accept or satisfactorily adjust himself to the suppression of these inner urges, emotional conflicts are aroused by conditions and circumstances over which he has no control. His efforts to establish himself, to be recognized and approved, and to function with a feeling of satisfaction and self-importance in the social group, are thwarted by inhibiting emotions. These become entangled with the switchboard of the nervous system that controls the process of talking. Instead of becoming an automatic, unconsciously directed habit formation, as do other bodily functions, talking is brought into consciousness and is held there to express in hesitant, stuttering speech the emotional struggle that is going on surreptitiously behind it.

It is of vital importance for the stutterer to become thoroughly familiar with the emotional aspects of his affliction, for it is in this realm of behavior that he is finding difficulty in facing social situations where speech is required. Not only is the tension exhibited in the organs of speech a needless and futile struggle, but just as unreasonable are the sham battles going on within the emotional life of the stutterer, warping his perception of reality, blinding his vision with fear, blocking the potential expression of his personality, and binding him to the mast of inferiority!

CHAPTER FIVE

Mental Cow Paths

ARE THE EARLY childhood experiences of the stuttering child peculiarly different from those of other children? Can they be clearly defined as difficult, unfortunate experiences which lead inevitably to the development of stuttering? No. Life, for every child, begins from the very day of birth to become a series of adjustments to the outside world and the people in it. No child, just because he does not develop stuttering or other nervous disorders, is necessarily exempt from the type of emotional adjustments which we consider to be the cause of conflict and inhibited speech.

Look for a moment through the glass door of a modern hospital. A babe in his crib, alone, isolated from his mother, suddenly awakens, aroused by hunger pains from within. (There was a day when an infant was fed whenever he was hungry, but this child is living in a very scientific age.) A chart on the wall reads that according to schedule this child will not be hungry for another thirty minutes. The babe's belief to the contrary is made more and more convincing by increasing pangs of hunger. He tries to kick up a fuss, but his movements are inhibited by carefully arranged clothing. He tries to get his little fists into his mouth, but these have been wrapped to prevent the habit of thumb-sucking. He finally gives vent to his emotions with shrieks of anger and tears of distress, while a nurse stands calmly by and comments upon the benefits of such vocal activity to his lungs. Sooner or later the child learns that such exhibitions avail him nothing, and if he is stubborn about it he is informed by more or less strenuous means that society will not tolerate them.

Swallowing displeasure, commonly called *repression* by the psychologist, cannot be avoided. The vital question is: "How do we take it, and what does it do to us?" We know that adults vary greatly in their ability or willingness to conform to the more and more exacting "dos" and "don'ts" of modern society. Some adults are very easy going, calm and self-controlled, and seem to have the ability to maintain their poise throughout the most severe domestic storms of everyday life. Others are always tired, irritable, out of patience, sensitive, moody, or neurotic, and are painfully upset by the slightest disturbance. And some of us stammer, or stutter, or withdraw from social obligations and hide behind false fortifications which we have constructed in defense of our weaknesses. The type of social adjustments which we make depends upon the physical, mental, and emotional habits we establish as basic patterns in early childhood. These patterns, however, depend not so much upon what our particular experiences have been or what catastrophes we have gone through as upon the nervous make-up with which we are endowed.

Nervous instability may be inherited—and this, by the way, is the only relationship between heredity and stuttering. Stuttering, as a symptom, is not inherited. The child of an adult stutterer may also stutter, either by direct imitation or through the inheritance of nervous instability from the parent who stutters. In other words, a child may inherit a predisposition to stutter because his nervous make-up is such that adjustments to persons and conditions in his early environment arouse constant emotional activity. For such a child everyday problems, which serve as a challenge to the courage and development of the average child, are made doubly difficult because the sensitive child must of necessity live with the temperamental parents or parent from whom he inherited his trait of emotional excitability. Suggestions, discipline, or advice are rarely administered in such a home without some degree of unfavorable emotional response from either the parent or the child.

We know that no two children of the same parents, even twins, inherit the same degree of emotionality. For one the slightest difficulty is extremely annoying, while for the other the same problem appears interesting and causes no particular emotional distress. My own children provide an excellent example of these differences. One is very sensitive, his feelings are easily hurt, he is fidgety and nervously impatient, and is quickly excited. From the very beginning his baby food failed to agree with him. He always cried as a child at the least provocation and later developed the habit of nail-biting as a release for his nervous tension. He stuttered badly for three years. The other boy had no trouble with the same baby food, has always been quiet and easy going, and seems to maintain a rare attitude of indifference toward situations that completely upset his brother.

We have learned that the nervous constitution
of a child may also be influenced by prenatal conditions, for it is during this period, from the third
week until birth, that the nerves in the body are
formed. Severe illness, malnutrition, alcoholism,
or other misfortunes of the mother may directly influence the development of the child, physiologi-
cally. Birth injuries, prolonged sieges of sickness
with infectious diseases, or serious shocks to the
nervous system during infancy may also cause nervous instability, subsequent emotional tensions,
and later, stuttering.

It has been said that all children stutter more or
less at some time during the speech forming period.
Between the babble stage and the time when children have mastered the control of their speech organs, it is very likely that all children stumble and
hesitate over new words which they are learning to
say. But the stuttering with which we are concerned, which becomes chronic and a permanent
impediment, is never accidental. It is a habit that
begins in the midst of an emotional conflict and is
almost immediately adopted as a special passport
into social situations. The child who is so nervously constructed that he is deeply aroused emotionally when his efforts to fulfill his inner desires
are thwarted, quickly loses the feeling of being "at

home in the world", and just as quickly accepts the feelings of insecurity, inferiority, and fear. He becomes sensitive and doubtful about his ability to cope with his environment. He develops a "cornered" attitude when his efforts to meet a situation and gain social approval are not immediately gratified. If stuttering presents a way out it is gladly adopted, unconsciously of course, by a mind that is in trouble, a mind that stays in trouble as long as it harbors the conviction, "I cannot succeed in this situation", and its faulty excuse, "because I cannot talk!"

As the adult stutterer faces his problem he is likely to be more concerned about his immediate feelings of anxiety, fear, and dread, as he has associated them with speaking situations, than with these emotional conflicts of childhood which he thinks he has successfully forgotten. Unfortunately, nothing that ever happens to us is ever forgotten, certainly not those events which are colored with strong feelings of distress. We consciously try to forget them, of course, for we seek to avoid unpleasant thoughts and emotions, just as we hasten to remove anything which irritates us physically. But we do not brush aside these unpleasant memories from our minds as we would brush an irritating spider web from the face. Instead we repress them into the memory retaining reservoir of the mind, the *unconscious*.*

The unconscious is the submerged level of the mind which serves as a storehouse for all wishes, desires, and memories of experiences, both happy and unhappy, which have been censored from con-scious thoughts because they are unpleasant or do not meet the approval of society. The unconscious also records and stores away all thoughts, feelings, attitudes, and emotions of the past, and to these from time to time are added new ideas which are similar to those already there. These associated ideas group together in what we call emotional complexes and are bound together by the emotion which is a part of the experiences which have been repressed. If fear of some nature became associ-ated with some unpleasant childhood experience, the same fear will arise in consciousness when a similar experience is repeated. Further than this we need not be concerned with what goes on with-in this unknown region of the mind.

To illustrate, a boy of seven has a terrible fear of the barber's chair. On his first visit to the bar-

---

*(We shall not be concerned with the controversy which is now going on between psychologists over the use of this term, nor shall we delve too deeply into the fascinating activities of the unconscious mind, as revealed by psychoanalysts; but for conven-ience sake, and for want of a better name, we shall think of the unconscious as the realm of mental activity that we know goes on but of which we are not consciously aware.)

ber he was elated and eager to get into the chair. Everything went well until he happened to glance above his head. When he saw the bright light directly over him, he suddenly became frightened and panicky. He ran from the chair, screaming, and refused to return. With the help of his father we traced back through the boy's experiences and discovered that when he was but two years of age he had suffered a painful mastoid operation. Something went amiss in the administration of the anesthetic and the child partially awakened before the operation was completed. His senses recorded the bright light above his head and associated with it the excruciating pain that was being inflicted by a man in white. The boy could remember nothing of the experience, but in the barber shop he saw the light and a man dressed in white, and with them he associated the pain he had suffered and had repressed into a complex of fear in the unconscious. The similarity of the barber shop to the hospital situation brought the original fear to the surface in consciousness, where it overruled all effort to master the barber shop situation.

Such is the birth of the emotional complex in the mind of the stutterer. Some incident of frustration or some painful event, which might have occurred very early in life, is repressed because the memory of it is unpleasant. This repression forms the nucleus for an emotional complex of anxiety in the unconscious. The disagreeable conflict is quickly dismissed from consciousness, but when other experiences of similar nature occur — and they do occur frequently for a sensitive, emotional child, who is prone to transform otherwise normal problems of daily life into emotional episodes—the idea of fear, submission, or whatever happens to be imbedded in the unconscious, creeps out and completely dominates the child's behavior. No physical effort, no amount of reasoning, determination, or power of consciousness can overpower these repressed emotions, as the stutterer well knows if stuttering has become the symptomatic expression of them.

One of my patients in Berkeley last summer, a girl of twenty, attending the University of California, complained of a terrifying fear of being pursued by a man in the darkness. She could in no way account for her fear, for she had never been attacked and her relationships with men had always been quite pleasant. She had never been afraid of the dark, she said, until she left home at the age of seventeen. For more than three years she had been afraid to go out alone at night for she felt that a man was following her; in fact, she thought at times that she could hear distinctly his footsteps behind her. She could well see on a

lighted street that no one was there, but nevertheless, she could not control this fear.

With the aid of her mother we traced this phobia to a childhood experience which the girl only
faintly remembered. When she was three years of
age she was chased by the gardener's boy into a
tool house and was playfully locked in. The boy
went home and forgot her. Many hours later,
after dark, she was found by searchers, curled up
against the inside of the tool house door, fast
asleep.

We can only guess what thoughts and tricks
of the imagination tortured the mind of this child
as she crouched in the darkness, fearing danger,
abandonment, and more than likely, death. Two
years later, when the girl entered kindergarten, she
began to stutter. Why? Going to school isn't
sufficient in itself to cause stuttering. How does
the advent of stuttering in this case become linked
with, or rather, become the outgrowth of the tool
house experience?

The child naturally forgot this episode as quickly
as possible, for the memory of it was disturbing
and unpleasant. The emotion of fear and its coun-
terpart, the feeling of insecurity, were repressed into the unconscious. At school, where the child
sensed a feeling of insecurity in the strange group
and in being away from her mother, the emotion

of fear came into consciousness and came into conflict with desires to be brave, to express herself, and
to be approved by the group. The disturbing conflict came to the fore when the girl was called upon
to speak, and disrupted normal habits of talking,
which were only partially developed. As stuttering set in, the emotional complex of fear and insecurity embedded in the unconscious found adequate expression in the conscious symptom of
hesitant, stumbling speech until the girl left the
protection and security of her home, at the age of
seventeen. Then as she ventured out into the
darkness alone, the feeling of insecurity revived the
full emotion of fear and brought up with it the feeling of being pursued by a man, as she was pursued
by the gardener's boy. The girl's stuttering naturally got worse as she withdrew into seclusion and
avoided social obligations which required her to go
out at night.

It would be a fortunate circumstance if unpleasant emotional states were confined strictly to the
act of talking, if the stutterer could keep his mind
free from dread during the intervals between actual speaking situations. Unfortunately, the fear
of "bugaboo" words keeps the stutterer emotionally stirred up most of the time. For twenty-five
years I never said the words: "water", "butter"
or "letter" once that I can remember without stut-

tering. I was thankful when oleomargarine made its appearance for then I could substitute "oleo" for all classes of butter, which I did in spite of the embarrassment I usually caused my hostess. I remember being stirred up emotionally for many hours preceding certain introductions which I knew I would have to make and in which I could not politely avoid saying my own name.

There are many harmful effects from such prolonged or frequently repeated periods of emotional strain. Glandular, visceral, and neuro-muscular activities, which normally go on automatically, are interfered with. Meals never digest properly when a person is nervous, excited, or affected by the emotion of fear. Physical tension becomes habitual, the stutterer feels awkward and ill at ease, and he becomes conscious of nervous sensations of which he should normally not be aware.

But this is not all. The most detrimental effect of these distracting emotional experiences, the one which only the speech therapist who has actually suffered with the affliction himself can fully comprehend, is the psychological warping of the personality which the stutterer inflicts upon himself. If the stutterer did not turn in upon himself, break down his self-confidence, saturate his mind with ideas of self-reproach, self-pity, inferiority, and inadequacy, and be guided constantly by the habits of worry, sensitiveness, and self-consciousness, the correction of stuttering would be a very, very simple procedure. Any stutterer could devise some trumped up method of talking by which he could slip over difficult bugaboo words, overcome his fear of them, establish a new complex of success and confidence in the unconscious, and soon re-establish fluent speech. In many cases, when the impediment is hardly noticeable or is cleverly covered up, and the stutterer has qualities other than speech which are greatly admired, there is no logical reason for these destructive attitudes to exist. But the stutterer magnifies his affliction in his own mind and dwells upon it so continuously that by his own suggestion he adds more and more complications to his problem.

The paradox of it all is that the exaggerated dread of stuttering, which looms up like a mountain of distress in the mind of the stutterer, was once a mere molehill of unpleasantness in the child mind. The stutterer must be willing to accept this interpretation, to blame no one but himself, to admit that his feelings of insecurity and inferiority have grown to their present proportions because he has permitted them to do so, through faulty ideas about himself and through blunders which he has made in adjusting himself to the world about him. With such an attitude and with the firm conviction that he need no longer follow these mental cow paths into brambles and thickets of anxiety and nervous tension, he should find no difficulty in following the open pathway to freedom, which we now approach.

vvv

CHAPTER SIX

The Stutterer Speaks!

No MATTER HOW MUCH I emphasize your
psychological readjustment program, I know only
too well that your immediate interest is in finding
a way to talk without stuttering. You can do this
in twenty minutes, or less, with a new fluency pattern of speech. I make this statement with assurance, for I have never found a stutterer who could
not speak fluently when thoroughly relaxed and
not consciously interfering with his speech. But I
admonish you not to depend upon this step alone,
for it is only a means toward an end. It is a successful means of eliminating the momentary dread
of stuttering, which is most paramount in your
mind; but your main objective is a well-adjusted

76

personality that will function harmoniously within
and in harmony with other human beings in everyday life, a personality that will face life with a feeling of power and confidence. This objective cannot be obtained through speech control alone.

No compromise can be made with any one of the
three equally important steps involved in the re-
establishment of free and fluent speech. Conscious
control must be exerted upon the fluency pattern
of speech in all speaking situations until it becomes
a habit. Emotional habits which have been work-
ing at cross-purposes in the past must be traced
through auto-analysis to their source, to the emotional atmosphere of childhood. Once recognized,
they must be condemned as misunderstood and un-
desirable influences and must be replaced with new
habits of emotional control. Faulty attitudes and
ideas which appear in the inventory of the present
personality must be scratched off in red ink and a
new mental hygiene program of positive, constructive ideas must be substituted and conscientiously
followed in all daily life situations. Now to a new
concept of speech.

Repeated practice in effortless, relaxed, and
smooth flowing speech will establish new auditory
and kinesthetic perceptions of talking. You must
actually hear and feel your voice gliding smoothly
over all speech sounds, concentrating on no sounds

or words in particular, but sensing the feeling of ease and passivity with every spoken word. Each successive experience will tend to relieve the tension and will gradually change the anticipation of blocking to a feeling of confidence in the smooth coordination of the speech organs.

RELAXATION, PHYSICAL AND MENTAL

Choose a quiet place where you know you will not be disturbed for at least fifteen minutes. Lie down on a couch or sit back in an easy chair, letting the body fall into a comfortable position. To younger people I suggest the limpness of a soft rag doll, devoid of any bodily movements. Rest the head in such a position that the lower jaw relaxes, the teeth sufficiently parted to admit the small finger between them. Close your eyes to shut out anything that might divert your attention, for this type of relaxation must be deeper than anything you have ever before attempted.

Think of each part of the body; first the feet, then the knees, abdomen, shoulders, face muscles, forehead, lips, and jaw muscles. Think of these parts of the body as being in the most relaxed state possible, absolutely still and quiet. Turn now to your breathing. Gradually slow down your breathing to approximately one-half your normal rate. Do not hold your breath after inhaling, for that tends to cause jerkiness, but permit the lungs to remain empty for a few seconds after exhaling. (If your shoulders move when you breathe you are not breathing correctly with the diaphragm but using only the apex of the lungs, a common fault of many stutterers. The abdomen must push out' ward on inhalation.) Think of stillness through' out the entire body as it rests quietly, loose and re' laxed. Continue to breathe slowly, deeply, from the diaphragm, assuming as nearly as possible the state of physical relaxation that you would reach in normal, sound sleep. Go back now to the be' ginning and repeat, step by step, the physical re' laxation of each part of the body until you feel the weight of yourself on the couch or in the chair.

After resting this way for a few minutes, recall in your mind the quietest place in which you have been and imagine that you are there. In doing this exercise I brought into mind the memory of a cer' tain sand dune in the desert, upon which I dropped to rest one clear, warm, summer evening. The sand was warm; no breeze was stirring; there was no noise from trains or autos — everything was quiet, peaceful, still. I found it easy to imagine that I was there, drowsy, restful, as still as the cac' tus plant, as immovable as the warm sand upon which I lay. Try to recall something similar to this in your own experience, a quiet lake, a still place in the mountains, or beside your fireplace, if you were there alone, in perfect silence. Recall as many details of the quiet experience as you can, relaxing more and more deeply all the while.

Do not be discouraged if it takes you ten minutes or longer the first few times to obtain the feeling of complete relaxation. It is an entirely new experience for some people, particularly those who never relax completely, even in sleep. Occasionally I find a child who, on account of unconscious resistances, is afraid to completely let go, afraid to release the tension which he has developed as a habit to brace himself for new situations. Remember that anxiety and tension go hand in hand. You have formed the habit of maintaining a certain degree of physical preparedness on account of your emotional states of dread and anxiety. You must learn to relax completely, even the muscles around the eyes, particularly the tongue, lips, and muscles of the lower jaw. Utter relaxation must be accomplished before the next steps are attempted, and you will know when you have reached it, for with the elimination of tension will come a new feeling of passivity, bringing with it a new sense of confidence and power.

THE FLUENCY PATTERN

What would happen if a man who couldn't swim were thrown into deep water? Almost every muscle and nerve in his body would go into action. He would become panicky, paw with his feet and flourish his arms, until by his own floun-dering he would sink himself. The experienced swimmer glides through the water with an *economy of effort*. One by one he has discarded the activity of a number of muscles which only hampered his progress through the water, until now the act of swimming is an effortless, smooth, rhythmic performance.

The stutterer tries to force out his words through a mechanism that is tense and taut. Ex-cessive muscular activity must be discarded until the act of talking becomes a habit of *allowing*—not forcing—the organs of speech to function with the least amount of energy possible. It will require considerable concentration in the beginning, but after a few practice periods the comfortable feeling of ease will be sufficient inducement to repeat.

With your head resting in such a position that the lower jaw is comfortably relaxed, begin with the sound of "ah", first in a soft whisper, then a little louder, permitting the breath to pour out naturally, without forcing. Disregard the sound

which you make—think only of making it without
effort. It will sound like a sigh, coming freely
through relaxed vocal cords, fading away as the
breath ceases. Repeat four or five times, slowly,
keeping in mind the relaxed feeling of the lips,
tongue, and jaw. Then begin counting in the same
way, slowly, one count to each breath, one . . . inhale, two . . . inhale, up to twenty. As you count
think of the breath stream as water pouring out of
a pitcher, unobstructed. Think of your words as
bits of ice flowing freely with the stream.

Now pause for a few moments, close your eyes,
and recall the sound and the feeling of ease with
which you said one of the words, the number
"seven", for instance. Recall that you did not
hiss out the initial "s" between tightened jaws.
The sound of "v" did not require needless pressure
of the lower lip against the upper teeth. The word
poured out smoothly, as effortlessly as the sound of
"ah". Count again from five to ten, exactly as
you did before, slowly, to confirm the impression
of ease and fluency.

In the same way continue with a poem of simple
meter, such as "Little By Little"; pause for a slow
breath at each comma:

"One step, and then another, and the longest walk,
        is ended;

One stitch, and then another, and the longest
    rent, is mended;
One brick, upon another, and the highest wall, is
    made;
One flake, upon another, and the deepest snow, is
    laid."

Be particularly careful to avoid any singsong
rhythm. This exercise is not intended to develop
a trumped up style of speech which you must always use in the future. Its sole purpose is to
change the ideas in both the conscious and unconscious, ideas which have become associated with
speech as a difficult, energetic, stumbling process,
to ideas of smooth and steady, effortless speech. If
you do not permit anxiety and tension to interfere,
your speech mechanism will function as perfectly
as it did before stuttering began, as effortlessly as
do the parts of your body which you use in walking.

After these steps in physical and mental relaxation and speech fluency have been practiced a few
times, vary the procedure as you wish. Choose a
few simple sentences such as you might be expected
to use in daily conversation, say them aloud with
the fluency pattern in mind, then close your eyes
and recall each sentence in its entirety, silently;
then repeat it again, aloud. The feeling of free-

dom and ease which you associate with these experiences in practice will soon establish new ideas
of confidence and faith in your speech machine,
where doubt and fear of failure have dominated in
the past. However, it will take many experiences
of success, many practice periods of relaxed, steady
control, before the act of effortless talking can be
turned over to the habit regions of the mind where
it belongs.

AUTOSUGGESTION

The deeper the feeling of relaxation, the more
susceptible is the unconscious mind to suggestion.
The efficacy of suggestion is based upon the sound
principle that any repeated thought in time becomes automatic in exactly the same way that repeated actions become unconsciously directed habits. In the past you have suggested failure with
your own thoughts; from now on you must constantly suggest confidence with thoughts of composure, calmness, courage, and faith in your speaking ability. Then you must carry out in life situations, by consciously living them out, the actions
which you suggest to yourself. The following suggestions are most effectively applied just before
falling asleep at night and during a short period of
relaxation after awakening in the morning. Think

them first, vary them to fit your individual case by attacking the attitudes which have disturbed you the most, and repeat them aloud, as indicated in the previous exercise:

"I have never felt so calm and peaceful."

"When I am calm within, my speech pours out freely."

"All talking can be just like this, smooth and free."

"I have the ability to maintain this passive feeling of composure and self-control at all times, no matter what happens about me."

"Each time I speak today I shall use as little effort as possible and permit my words to flow with ease, slowly, through relaxed lips."

Each day choose a word like "poise", "composure", "self-confidence", "coolness", or "tranquillity", and in your spare moments think of some opportunity to apply it in your routine activities. Perhaps you drive through heavy traffic on your way to work in the morning. Leave home ten minutes earlier than usual, drive considerably slower than you ordinarily drive, and see how relaxed you can be in spite of the noise and congestion about you. You will be surprised to see in the example of others the amount of energy which is needlessly wasted.

For the same reason that two objects cannot occupy the same space at the same time, two opposite thoughts cannot simultaneously be present in consciousness. While you are thinking calmness and self-control, ideas of fear, worry, or haste cannot dominate your mind and direct your actions. The same holds true for the imagination. It is here that you have built up much of your anxiety, from the fear of breaking down, of appearing ridiculous, of betraying an impediment of which some one may not as yet be aware. More of your anxiety than you realize is caused by your imagining a dilemma beforehand. The irony of it all is that the whole dreaded barrier of speech blocking is in itself only an invention of the imagination. To wit, a stutterer once said to me, "I simply cannot say the word 'seven' ". Yet he spoke it perfectly in telling me that he could not say it.

Build up your imagination with ideas of confidence and success, with the expectancy of cool serenity and control, and it will work for you constructively more effectively than it has worked against you, for it will be fortified with desire, ambition, and determination. Don't wait until a speaking situation is upon you; assume the role of poise and relaxed composure before you meet it. Visualize yourself speaking with positive self-assurance, with the fluency pattern at your command. Such constructive visualization will of necessity keep out of your mind the dreaded anticipation of fear and failure.

I repeat that the fluency pattern of speech is but a means toward an end, only one step in your re-construction program. It serves its purpose well in changing the ideas toward speech, in replacing the false idea, "I can't", with the positive convic-tion, "*I can!*", but it will be dropped in due time as the habit region of the mind takes over the duty. Remember, however, that habits are interfered with by emotional conflict. No matter how strongly you build up a habit of relaxed speech fluency, it will not serve as the mouthpiece for a warped and inhibited personality. If you rely up-on it as a crutch to carry you through all speaking situations without attending to the rehabilitation of your whole personality as you go along, you will learn as I did that you have major adjustments far removed from the control of speech to deal with before your problem is permanently solved. The fluency pattern applies to living, physically, men-tally, and emotionally, to character and personality just as much as to the control of the mouthpiece through which social contacts are made.

CHAPTER SEVEN

What Happened Then?

THE MOST DECEITFUL, the most illusionary, and yet the most potent enemy of mankind is fear. Only one person with whom I have discussed this subject ever claimed absolute immunity from fear. This man's wife told me later that during the depression he had made himself almost sick from the fear of losing his job. He had worked many hours overtime against the will of his boss, not to insure his position, as he thought, but to combat the fear in his imagination of losing it.

Some suffer more than others, from more fears or worse ones, but few have suffered greater distress from any fear, real or imaginary, than I suffered from the fear of strangling, claustrophobia.

The last time it terrorized me was when I was just beginning, seven years ago, to make the personality readjustments which you are about to make. I decided immediately to trace it to its source.

I had driven approximately halfway through the Third Street tunnel in Los Angeles when the car ahead of me collided with a large truck. Autos streamed in from both ends of the tunnel, horns honking and exhausts saturating the air with smoke. Suddenly I became panicky. A feeling of suffocation gripped me, I felt dizzy and faint, and then everything began to turn black. I was getting out of my car, intending to run away from the scene, when the traffic started moving. Somehow I managed to control my car until I reached fresh air at the end of the tunnel. I was trembling, dripping cold perspiration, weak from fear. I noticed that other people were apparently unaffected, some were laughing, and I thought they were laughing at me.

This experience caused me to recall very vividly the similar feeling which for more than two years had kept me out of the barber's chair. I was being shaved one day, resting quietly with a hot towel over my face, when suddenly I felt that I was strangling. I jerked the towel from my face and took a deep breath. I laughed with the barber about my paleness, but I resolved to avoid that situation again. While thinking over the details of this experience I was reminded of one of somewhat similar nature which had occurred many years before.

Two years after I left the army a prolonged siege of inflammatory rheumatism sent me to the hospital. I sweltered in Turkish baths for a month with no relief. A specialist was called in to examine me and finally decided that my tonsils were to blame, so I was prepared for the simple operation of removing them. Everything went normally until one of the doctors clamped a heavy piece of gauze over my nose and began dripping ether upon it. I became nauseated, begged for a breath of air, and then became hysterical. I was told later that two doctors, a nurse, and an interne had all they could do to hold me until the ether took effect. While chiding me the next day about my childish antics, the doctor suggested that I must have been gassed during the war. No, but I did wear a "flu" mask, and one day while marching I was severely reprimanded by my company officer for not wearing it tightly over my nose. So my fear went further back than that.

When I was four years of age an orphan cousin came to live with us. He was older than I and was without a doubt one of the meanest boys who ever carried a sling shot. His greatest pleasure seemed to be to torture me and make me cry. According to my mother, who surprised him in the act, he one day caught me and clasped his hands over my mouth and nose so that I could neither cry nor breathe. He all but strangled me to death before my mother came to the rescue. I could recall nothing of this experience, though I remembered the lad well. I recall how I hated him and how joyfully I had seen him depart for the reform school.

Could this have been the original nucleus of my phobia? Here was I, a man of thirty, susceptible at any moment in a theater, elevator, tunnel, or in any closed place, to the fear of suffocation, forced to surrender in spite of my conscious efforts to ignore the feeling. Other people had no fear in these situations, I reasoned, but hadn't I reasoned this way each time I was caught and still had found no solution to my fear?

It was then that I ran across in my reading a book which I shall cherish as long as I live, *Secret Springs,* by Harvey O'Higgins. Between its covers I read — and it reads like a novel — that the world is full of people who are troubled with fears similar to mine. I read that these fears are caused by infantile impressions, usually resulting from the repression of some instinctive emotion, that the emotional distress could be relived again, and that, by building up a familiarity with the thing or condition feared, the conflict could be brought vividly into consciousness and there be drained off.

I was satisfied that I had found the root of my fear complex. I must now revive the conflict and reason it out with adult judgment, with sensibility and wisdom which I did not have at the age of four. I could not recall a single detail of the episode so I conjured up a scene that would fit the experience. I reproduced in my mind a picture of the yard and surroundings, which I could remember clearly, where the scene probably occurred. I fitted my obstreperous cousin and myself into the picture and then imagined that I was being choked. I went through all of the details of the struggle as it probably took place, until I actually sensed the feelings of fear and helplessness which a child of four would feel at the mercy of such a tormentor. From the picture which I had drawn in my imagination I could easily understand the anguish which I had suffered; in fact, I became tense and nervous and highly emotional as I revived the details of the experience.

This, I reasoned, happened to me when I was a child, helpless, a victim of circumstances over which I had no control. I had buried the emotion of fear and the feeling of insecurity below the threshold of consciousness when I was four years

old, and now these childish impressions were finding their way into consciousness in the weirdest
fashion and in the strangest of places. Intangible,
imaginative, fantastical, yet so dominating—need I
longer be driven from reality by such illegitimate
creations of the child mind? I had but one test to
make, to face a situation squarely while my mind
was open for conviction, while the revival of the
emotional complex had opened wide the doorway
to the unconscious for the penetration of truth and
fact.

I went directly to a dark clothes closet and shut
myself in. I dropped the key to the floor and
kicked it into a corner. Then I imagined that I
was in an elevator, one of my most dreaded situations, and waited. Before long the choking sensations began. I felt that I couldn't breathe,
although I knew that the closet was full of oxygen.
Then I placed my hands on my chest and discovered, to my amazement, that I was not breathing! I was actually holding my breath—the fear
had stopped the process of inhaling air into my
lungs. I stooped for the key and was about to surrender when I noticed a crack of light under the
door. Air, I argued, was entering there. I drew a
long, deep breath, then another, and then I
yawned, gloriously, for I realized that with that
yawn of relaxation I had banished forever from my

imagination my most dreaded fear, claustrophobia. Since that night I have never avoided dark or closed places. Riding elevators is a pleasant thrill and driving through tunnels always fascinates me.

In general, this is the procedure of auto-analysis. What happened to you in childhood to make you afraid of facing life? You are not concerned with the day or the event in which your stuttering started. Whatever caused the emotional conflict, shock, fear, suppression of an instinctive desire, the loss of a parent through death or divorce, severe disciplinary treatment, ridicule of something you did, or even a foolish fairy tale, might have been hidden away in the unconscious for many months or years before it found its way back into consciousness to disrupt your speech. You must search through the emotional atmosphere of your childhood for the experiences which led you to react toward other persons with one of two feelings, either the *feeling of insecurity* or the *feeling of inferiority*. It was from one or both of these strong feelings that you laid down a pattern of emotional reactions to guide you in future social situations, a pattern which you have followed ever since.

Begin with the feelings and emotional habits which now cause you distress in meeting and conversing with other persons. The significant fact is that you become disturbed in speaking situations, in the presence of other people, never when you are sure that you are alone. With whom do you find it most difficult to converse? In which group do you feel most comfortable and at ease? Why do you mistrust your ability to measure up to those persons who cause you the most distress when you attempt to speak? What arouses your anger, jealousy, contempt, or sympathy in a social situation? With whom do you converse more easily, men or women?

It is true that some of your present feelings and emotional attitudes exist only because you stutter, but those which most frequently undermine your selfconfidence and your sense of wellbeing in the presence of others date back to emotional experiences which upset you in childhood. One characteristic of the period of early childhood is that it is extremely emotional. Healthy development calls for the release of these tensions, a release which you found in outbursts of laughter or tears or temper, until those persons whom you annoyed stepped in with adult standards of control and forced you to suppress your emotions, particularly your vocal expressions. You were a sensitive child, easily excited, easily discouraged, impatient when your desires were postponed, and quickly disappointed, and for *you* swallowing displeasure meant conflict. Doubting your ability to cope with your environment, fearing to face new situations with courage and determination, silently forsaking offensive tactics and placing yourself on the defensive, you began storing away, probably long before stuttering became serious, unhealthy attitudes of inferiority and weakness.

Solicit the cooperation of your family or any other living relatives who were familiar with conditions in your childhood environment, and try to the best of your ability to disentangle the threads of emotional conflict that go deep into your unconscious storehouse. Bear in mind that your environment at that time was made up of a very small social group, of possibly not more than a dozen persons outside of your own family. In the atmosphere created by such a small group you began comparing yourself and found yourself wanting in their presence.

Are you unduly self-conscious and sensitive? Are your feelings easily hurt? Did you have an older brother or sister, or was there a neighbor child, who made life difficult for you? Was there any distinguishing feature about you, your appearance, your awkwardness, your quick temper, or something else that attracted the attention and comments of your playmates? Were you as a child the bearer of such nicknames as "Fatty", "Skinny", "Freckles", "Four-eyes", or "Percy"?

If so, did you fight about it, or did you become shy and reticent and harbor a grudge against those who chided you? Irvin S. Cobb has made his homeliness one of his richest assets, but not many of us who were made sensitive about some slight peculiarity in childhood have learned to accept our shortcomings sensibly.

When I began analyzing my personality traits I realized that I was pitifully self-conscious and over-sensitive. As I reflected upon the impressions which I had formed in childhood about my personal appearance, some of the peculiarities of which I have mentioned, I revived a number of emotional experiences. The one that stood out most clearly was a scene in which first I threatened to decapitate a certain Johnny Mallers, and then attempted to do so. I remember that I started the fight because he called me "tight-breeches" in the presence of my playmates. I picked myself up a few minutes later, wondering what had hit me, but that is not my point. I carried the nickname and a hatred in my heart throughout the rest of that school year, and at the same time I unwittingly added resentment and sensitivity to a rapidly growing complex of self-consciousness. Childish impressions! And now I was sensitive in the same way about baldness. Something had to be done about it, something sensible and constructive.

I decided to develop a sense of humor—an entirely new addition to my personality make-up—
about my cranial deficiency. Getting wrought up
over a few straggling wisps of what was once an
exuberant growth of blonde hair, a condition
which nothing in the world could remedy, had
only antagonized more comments, usually from
those who were no better off than I. I started a
collection of jokes about baldness and added to it
a number of original witticisms. Nothing has
brought me more amusement and now no one
relishes bald-headed jokes more than I. Needless
to say my new attitude soon relegated self-consciousness along with my fear of closed places into
the discard.

What is your attitude toward your employer
and other superiors?   How do you take instruc-
tions and respond to authority? Do you become
antagonistic toward some new routine or new adjustment in your business? Is your inner attitude
one of full cooperation? If not, are you justified
in your stubbornness, and is it paying you dividends? Do you react with fear or anger when you
are reprimanded for some mistake you have made?

You will find some of the answers in the feelings
which you had toward your father or some other
dominant person in your childhood environment.
Be honest with yourself, for you must come to

some decision as to why you feel inferior to certain persons, and you will fail to find the right one if you cover up your true feelings with sentiment. Think about your father's influence upon your childhood life. When, how, and why did he arouse you emotionally? Do not feel guilty if you hated him occasionally. It is no crime for an innocent child inwardly to hate a parent who whips him unmercifully, frightens him into submission, ridicules his efforts with sarcasm, mistreats his mother with physical or mental cruelty, or compares him unfavorably with another child who never gets into trouble and always succeeds!

If your conscience will not permit you, in your search for important influences upon your early emotional life, to condemn candidly certain mistakes which your parents made, unwittingly, sincerely believing that their tactics were the best for your welfare, you have an important adjustment to make. It is no disgrace to admit your faults and theirs, if you are willing to do something about it. Patriarchal monarchy, which permits the father to domineer the home situation and rule with an iron hand, is still popular in the home of Puritan ancestry. Its failures and tragedies, however, cannot be ignored by those who have come to the understanding that for healthy mental development each mem-

ber of the family constellation is entitled to equal
rights of self-expression and individuality.

In my personality readjustment program I found
that this influence of which I have been speaking
was one of the most difficult to overcome. I finally
had to admit that there were times when I hated
my father, bitterly, for what seemed to me to be
unfair domination. At last, deep down in my
heart, I made a satisfactory adjustment which for-
gave all of the mistakes of those who had the guidance of my childhood in their hands, but mind you,
not until I had removed all sentimentality and had
honestly revived all of the destructive emotional
attitudes which grew out of unfortunate home experiences. You must not slight this adjustment if
you are to solve your faulty attitudes toward
superiors. Remember that stuttering is a password
for the feeling of inferiority, a feeling without
which you would likely never have found cause to
falter in speech.

What did you fear the most in childhood, darkness, water, animals, people, or God? You were
not born afraid of these things. If you learned any
of these fears you undoubtedly did so under emotional circumstances. Had you cause for feelings
of physical insecurity? Were you a sickly child?
Did you fall heir to all of the contagious diseases
to which children are susceptible? If so, you had

few opportunities to develop self-reliance and independence, and you were probably over-coddled far past the time when you should have become reasonably dependent upon yourself. The most frequently recurring episode in your dreams, such as falling, being chased by animals or other objects, or hearing loud and shrieking noises, may help you to discover some emotional experience that left its indelible mark upon your unconscious pattern of behavior. Some type of fear is practically always behind the symptom of stuttering, so survey carefully the environment in which some of these fears might have been established.

Finally, what were your early sexual experiences? Your personality reconstruction must clear up all attitudes of shame and self-reproach, for you will not get far toward freedom and harmonious adjustment to other persons if you are burdened with a guilty conscience. Your conscience regarding sex matters is not established by what you have done. It is fabricated from your attitudes toward the things you have or have not done, and these attitudes have all been forced upon you by modern conventions and standard social ideals. You inherited no moral understanding of right and wrong. If you made mistakes you learned about them from those who had developed a strong sex conscience, sometimes a painful one.

The implications of sex development are too many to mention here, but we must consider the faulty impressions which so often cause distress in the mind of the innocent child. Intimate love scenes and demonstrations between parents in the presence of the child breed jealousy, resentment, or even hatred if the child is sensitive and clings too dependently to the bond of mother love. Sharp reproval when curiosity seeks satisfaction, or shame and condemnation when sexual interest becomes aroused, leads to no end of emotional conflict. Masturbation, a common phenomenon in both sexes, in itself a habit which is nothing more than a useless waste of energy, considered by physicians to have no harmful physical effects, dangerous only in the attitudes of guilt and self-reproach which it creates, need not cause us to shudder. There is no such thing as being over-sexed excepting in one's thoughts and ideas, and then only in perversion based upon inadequate knowledge. Sex is basically a creative urge. With understanding and a little conscientious guidance it can be directed into worthy channels which will give intensely more satisfaction than can ever be gained from perverted abuse.

Become as familiar as you possibly can with the emotional aspects of your early sex life, involving all love relationships, and you will more than likely uncover one of the reasons why you have struggled through social situations with trepidity. Be critical, the more critical the better, bearing in mind that you are criticizing a nervous, sensitive, ignorant child of the past. Study your emotional life and see if you can justify any of these childish impressions, by which you are now being guided in making social adjustments, as adequate stimuli for your present responses in speaking situations. Familiarity with your faulty emotional habits will greatly reduce your fear of them—then do something about them! Face your problems as you know them and prove to yourself that with adult courage, judgment, and conviction, you can be master over all imaginary creations of a child mind.

‿‿‿‿‿‿‿‿‿‿‿‿‿‿‿‿‿‿‿‿‿‿‿‿‿‿‿‿‿‿‿‿‿‿‿‿

CHAPTER EIGHT

Freedom

WHEN I LEFT THE AUDITORIUM that night, seven years ago—where I left you at the end of chapter two—I was convinced for the first time that my problem went far deeper than the mere symptom of stuttering, toward which I had always directed my attention. I hardly knew just where to begin, but it was encouraging to learn of the psychological implications of my impediment. It gave me a new hope of removing it with an entirely new approach when all others had failed. I had heard of emotions, instincts, personality, and self-confidence, but strangely I had never associated these realms of behavior with my stuttering.

My first decision was to become thoroughly ac-

quainted with the psychological aspects of talking
and with all phases of mental activity that were in
any way related to speaking situations. Before I
was satisfied that I knew enough about myself to
attempt the correction of my impediment two
months had gone by and I had read more than
eighty books, only one of which dealt directly with
the problem of stuttering. I was not to be content
with the opinions of others who had never gone
through the experiences of stuttering themselves,
but rather was determined to work out my own
solution by studying my own reactions and emotional habits in the presence of other persons. It
was then that I accomplished the rehabilitation of
fluent speech in the short period of five weeks.

My course of procedure followed two main ob-
jectives. First, in order to change the association
of ideas regarding speech, I held in the focus of
conscious attention the fluency pattern which I de-
scribed in chapter six. Every speaking situation
became an experiment, a testing opportunity for
the application of conscious control, not only
speech control, but emotional control as well. Sec-
ondly, not in order of importance, but hand in
hand with the faithful application of a complete
fluency pattern, I carried on a personality reconstruction program. This program, based upon
sound principles of mental hygiene, served as a

clearing house for the psychological warpings and misguided emotions which had driven me more and more into conflict with society. And to this program of emotional re-birth I attribute the greatest share of my success.

I began with an inventory of my personality characteristics, my complete physical, mental, and spiritual make-up. I made a list of my assets and liabilities, a sort of character sketch of the self which was about to be remodeled. I tried to view my personality objectively, as I appeared to my acquaintances, and subjectively, as I knew my real inner self. My inventory was an amazing revelation, particularly the criticisms which were contributed by my wife. It really looked more like the description of a worm than of a human being! If you will be as honest as I was in recording every personal trait that has made social adjustment a struggle for you, and if you can get the candid opinions of anyone as critical as was my wife, I can assure you that your inventory will serve as a challenge to you to begin immediately making some drastic changes.

This is what I found in *mental liabilities*: — a phobia of closed places, worry, pessimism, self-consciousness, skepticism, indecision, suspicion, dread, fear, self-pity, impatience, stubbornness, quick temper, extreme sensitivity, selfishness, intolerance, jealousy, shallow desires, thoughtlessness of others, resentment, hate, and feelings of inferiority and inadequacy. Count them—twenty-three!

Next I examined the body in which this discordant mind had been trying to function. This is what I found in *physical liabilities*:—tense and strained muscles, nervousness, headaches, backaches, insomnia, nervous indigestion, laziness, constant fatigue, poor posture, slovenly personal habits, fidgetiness, irritability, lack of physical initiative, a strained expression on my face, and a very high, rapidly receding forehead.

Spiritually—I found nothing to which I could cling with any degree of security or faith. I had no use for people who went to church and professed Christianity. I tried to make myself believe that they were hypocrites, but the real reason I disliked them was because inwardly I knew that I was a worse hypocrite than any of them! I had heard that things in the Bible were not true, that scientists made no allowance for an immortal God, but I had not learned that all science ultimately reaches a stopping point and concedes the rest to the handiwork of a Supreme Being.

My personality assets were few, but worth mentioning. I did discover six feet of body, which, if straightened vertically and sufficiently inflated with egotism, might assume the lofty proportions of a

dignified gentleman.   One of my greatest assets
was, of course, my new understanding of the problem which I had always considered to be only stuttering.   I also had a willingness to sacrifice anything for the consummation of my immediate task.
I had an unflinching determination to become
master of myself, to make a complete personality
change, and to make a permanent habit of self-
control.   I had utter faith in such a procedure that
would carry me through all situations, no matter
how disturbing.

I have told you what happened to my worst
fear, the phobia of strangling in closed places.
Worry came next.   Worry?   I believe I inherited
that trait.   My father was undoubtedly the
champion worrier west of the Rockies — until I
took the championship away from him.   He paid
his grocery bill a dozen times each month, while
the grocer received his check but once.   My father
always worried about the uncertainty of the
future, about that inevitable crisis when sickness or
tragedy would be certain to strike and send us all
to the poorhouse.   Under the circumstances it was
utterly impossible for him to lay aside any more
than a small amount of life insurance security, and
constant worry didn't help matters one bit.   It did
teach me, a sensitive child, to grow up with con-

siderable apprehension of adult life and its respon-
sibilities.

All stutterers are to some extent worriers.
Worry has never solved a single problem for you.
It is a useless waste of energy, a substitution for
doing something, an excuse commonly resorted to
by weaklings. Lord Dewar says that, "Worry is
interest paid on trouble before it comes due."
Isn't it true that the things we worry about the
most never come to pass? We might as well be
happy and keep our senses clear from the clouds of
worry until something really does happen. We
will be much more fit to cope with trouble if it
comes our way. Judicious planning and clear-
minded precaution go a long way toward prevent-
ing disaster, but a mind that is filled with worry
does a poor job of thinking ahead.

For more than ten years I worried about arthritis. Who wouldn't worry about a rapidly
spreading, permanent stiffening of the joints? I
had sprained my back one day while loading boxes
of oranges on a truck. I was examined by an old-
fashioned country doctor, whom many thought
would have been a first class veterinary. He told
me that he had been studying about this malicious
disease of the joints and was wondering when he
would find a patient with its symptoms. Then I
walked in and fell heir to arthritis! For many

years I moved my spine as cautiously as if it were made of stick candy, but I often wondered how it managed to remain flexible most of the time. Finally I went to a modern physician, had an X-ray picture taken of my sacro-iliac joint, and went home with it tightly strapped. Since the sprain healed a few weeks later I have never given my back another conscious thought.

I realize that economic insecurity is one of the most prevalent causes for worry, but worry will not improve the situation any and you will only make life harder for yourself and for those about you by worrying. Your future will be more hopeful than you ever anticipated if you will refuse to worry and instead begin thinking about all of the things you have in this world for which you should be thankful. *You* cannot afford to worry, so put hopefulness, a feeling that things will come out for the best, in its place.

Pessimism is closely related to worry. According to my dictionary pessimism is the disposition to take the least hopeful view of things, the doctrine that the pains of life overbalance its happiness. This was my point of view as a stutterer, of course, for I had become well acquainted with discouragement. I only hope that you have not been as big a fool as I was in this respect. Every summer for many years I was allowed one week for a vacation, for rest and recreation, but because I was a pessimist I always turned it into an annual expect-hard-luck week. First, I almost drove my family into distraction trying to decide where we would go. I knew that the fish wouldn't bite here and the roads would be terrible there, at least four of my five tires would blow out, and one of us would be sure to get sick. I loaded the car down with tire patches, tow chains, aspirin tablets, all kinds of precautions against trouble, until there was little room left for equipment that we could enjoy. Nothing of any consequence ever happened, but nevertheless I succeeded in making life miserable for all of us until we were safely parked at home again.

Optimism is a state of mind, closely related to faith, and an attitude which the stutterer must adopt if he intends to complete the reconstruction of his personality. It doesn't cost a cent, and you won't rob anyone by using it. You will undoubtedly make someone else happier if you adopt it as a living philosophy. All the while you will be clearing up the complex of anxiety that has nursed along your habit of stuttering. Look for thoughtfulness and kindness in others and you will not fail to find it. Scratch off pessimism from your liabilities and write in optimism under assets. You will be repaid in big dividends of self-assurance and happiness.

Perhaps I have missed you with fear, worry, and pessimism. If so, your task is much easier than was mine. But I shall not pass you by with self-consciousness, for this I am positive is a characteristic trait of all stutterers. Whatever personality thwartings you have been able to adjust, your frequent experiences of failure and humiliation have built upon the foundation of insecurity and inferiority a strong attitude of self-consciousness in the presence of other persons. This vexatious habit is nothing more than wondering what other people are thinking of you, but it can become an awful barrier in making friends and keeping them. It was one of my most serious handicaps, a habit which was easily traced to childhood influences. My queer clothing, odd haircuts, lunches wrapped in newspapers, the clumsy shoes I wore, all drew attention from my playmates. As an adult I was always suspicious when someone laughed that I was the object of ridicule. When people whispered or cast side remarks in a group I was sure that they were talking about me. Always thinking in terms of myself, interpreting the success of others as reflections upon me, afraid to look people straight in the eye, and always feeling ill at ease on account of my stuttering, I had what seemed to be a difficult adjustment to overcome self-conscious-ness.

It was easy. At the first bridge party I attend-ed I made up my mind to become interested in each individual in the group, their clothes, their actions, their hands, and their speech, to see what impres-sions they made upon me. I was to do very little talking; I was not to use the pronoun "I", or direct in any way the conversation or attention of others toward myself; I was not to get provoked, excited, or emotionally aroused, no matter what happened; I was to be gracious, polite, and thoughtful of the comfort of others; I was to maintain a calm, cool composure.

The result was a revelation, more than I had hoped for. Friends whom I had always considered well-poised became fidgety under my calm and steady observation. Little tricks of nervousness betrayed their uneasiness. This was a startling discovery for me, that other people were not confi-dently at ease in a mixed group, no more so than I. I had failed to notice this before because I had al-ways been too busy thinking about myself. Grad-ually I became aware of a new feeling of super-iority, a feeling I had never sensed before in such a group. It was not long until I was entering into the conversation, calmly, confidently, and not stut-tering! I kept in mind the pattern of fluency, I listened, and I thrilled at the sound of my own voice, low, steady, relaxed, and free!

When I left that party I had a new understanding of self-confidence and self-respect. I knew that I had found myself, the new self, no longer inferior, no longer overwhelmed with inhibitions, no longer to be intimidated by false attitudes manufactured in my own mind. I visualized for myself a new goal. I visualized a superior personality, one of unusual composure and self-assurance. I decided to assume the role of such a personality, possessing rare self-control, believing that if I persevered in my efforts to appear courageous, confident, relaxed, and at peace with the world, the habit of living this way would eventually mould into reality a true state of serenity and harmony within. This decision I believe had more to do with my success than all of the other things which I did during those five weeks.

I found in a very short time that this matter of living day by day can be an unbelievably peaceful and happy adventure instead of a continuous struggle, spiced with temperamental eruptions, tension, discord, and nervousness, *if we make habits of relaxation and self-control*. Do not be afraid that slowing down will decrease your efficiency. It will increase it many times over, for you will rise above the confusion and turmoil of aimless haste

which now retards your progress. By maintaining
a feeling of relaxation you will move with pre-
cision, preserve your energy, and think with clear-
ness and deliberation. You will make definite
plans and carry them out efficiently, and accom-
plish far more than you ever have before in the
same amount of time. You will live in a state of
mind that finds no need for faltering speech.

But I have not finished my story. When I drew
a line through a mental liability I entered its opposite under assets; self-confidence for self-consciousness, tolerance for intolerance, self-respect for self-
pity, etc. A month had passed and my stuttering
had practically disappeared, but I had not yet dealt
with hate, temper, and skepticism. I had learned
to hate certain people who had openly humiliated
me about my stuttering. I would have to do something about my fiery temper, but I knew that an
occasion for that adjustment would soon arise. I
was skeptical about God. I had tried to be boldly
indifferent, to believe that it didn't matter, that I
could get along just as well without a religious
faith, but at the same time I was afraid of my attitude, sensing the insecurity of floundering about in
the quicksands of atheism. I knew that I would
have to make some adjustment with God.

Perhaps the day shall come when I can completely forgive those who ridiculed and imitated

my stuttering. As yet I have failed to find any more excuse for this than for laughing at the crippled or the blind. I believe that those who torment the stutterer do so to compensate for some weakness or shortcoming of their own, and taunting the stutterer does provide one situation in which they can appear superior. If they only knew of the pain of living in constant fear, fear of breaking down, fear of appearing ridiculous and losing the respect of desired friends, and if they knew of the number of stutterers who isolate themselves from society in solitary occupations, simply because some thoughtless person made light of their affliction, they would cease to be so apathetic and heartless. I have no sympathy with the radio or screen entertainer who finds no better way of making a living than to imitate those who cannot help their affliction.

It is true that I have made friends, outwardly, with those whom I once hated. Yet, in their presence I cannot help but sense a slight emotional reaction, of disgust perhaps, nevertheless unpleasant.

I had a volcanic temper, one that erupted at the slightest provocation. In the throes of anger I was like a chained beast, bursting with tension and nervous energy, blinded by an almost uncontrollable fury. My temper burst forth one morning when my tractor failed to start. I cranked until

I was exhausted, cursed and kicked the iron beast, and then sat down to cool off. My dog, who had slinked off at the harsh sound of my voice, returned sheepishly and took my mind away from the tractor for a moment. I suddenly felt prompted by an unconscious habit to make sure that I had turned on the priming gas. No, I hadn't! For fifteen exasperating minutes I had been flooding the motor with distillate, and tractors don't start on cold mornings with distillate. While I waited for this fuel to partially evaporate, I pondered over the childishness of my actions . . . . I had become impatient because I was late . . . . In my haste to make up lost time my emotions had interfered with the habitual procedure of turning the fuel pet cock to the priming gas . . . Exactly, I reasoned, as the stutterer emotionally interferes with the unconscious process of talking.

It has been difficult at times to control my temper, but every time I have succumbed to anger I have regretted my weakness. It is possible through practice to eliminate anger and quick temper by substituting self-control. For you it is of vital importance to do away entirely with this virulent emotion, and I assure you that it can be done through relaxation and patience.

This matter of self-control impressed me deeply because in practice it gave me a sense of well-being and a new feeling of strength and power. I tested its practical application by creating situations, such as inquiring about tires which I didn't need, discussing a new car with an automobile salesman, and striking up friendly conversations with mere acquaintances on the street. I thought the word *self-control*, repeated it aloud, scribbled it on my tractor, printed it on my desk-blotter, saw it in my imagination, and I lived it. I even wrote a poem about it, which I carried with me for weeks to remind me of my greatest adjustment.

*   *   *

When you think of the power in nature,
    Or the strength of a wave in the sea,
When you think of the force of a river,
    Or the might of a towering tree,
When you look at the stars in the heavens,
    And wonder what keeps them in place,
Do you think of the Infinite Power
    That silently guides through space?

Do you know that you too have within you,
    As great as the greatest of these,
A silent and powerful servant
    That no one but you can release?
When you need it the most, it will serve you
    When you stand with your back to the wall,
It is always awaiting your summons,
    "Self Control" is the number you call!

You will find it in calm concentration,
   In silence and stillness it reigns;
It will not permit hurry and worry
   To make mountains where there should be plains.
When fear and anxiety grip you,
   And a worried frown wrinkles your face,
Just relax and relieve nervous tension,
   Let calm SELF-CONTROL take its place.

* * *

What happened to my physical liabilities I cannot tell you, for I do not know. Aside from attending to my backaches I did nothing, consciously. With a growing sense of self-assurance and confidence my posture gradually changed from slouchy stoop-shoulderedness to erectness. Nervousness, indigestion, fatigue, headache, and insomnia disappeared as I ceased to give them conscious attention and as emotional control took the place of emotional interference. Fidgetiness and irritability gave way to quiet composure and relaxation. Laziness changed to vitality as new ambitions and constructive ideas saturated my mind.

Each day I started out with a definite program, and this, kind reader, is where you are most likely to fall down. It is difficult to slow down in an atmosphere of haste and excitement, but it is absolutely necessary, not only every day but every minute of the day, until the tensions which cause

stuttering have disappeared. I arranged for as
many practice periods as possible, in which I practiced relaxation and the pattern of fluency. I visualized ahead each speaking situation as I expected
it to arise during the day, and while I was relaxed
I repeated aloud as nearly as I could anticipate the
conversation which might ensue. I slowed down
in everything I did. I dressed slowly, walked
slowly, ate my meals considerably slower than ever
before, and I talked slowly. I stayed away from
all shows and exciting influences until I was absolutely sure that I could maintain an emotional tranquillity, no matter what might happen in my presence. I made an effort to be cheerful at all times,
to be fully cooperative with everyone, to be
thoughtful and considerate, and above all, opti-
mistic.

I continued—and am still continuing—my reading, the best of which I have included in the biblio-
graphy of this book. I overworked the mental
process of suggestion, or better, autosuggestion, by
repeating over and over again during the day such
constructive statements as, "I know that as long as
I maintain a feeling of relaxation I can speak perfectly", and, "I know that I can be just as calm
and undisturbed in the presence of others as I am
now, while alone and relaxed." I resolved that no
matter how pitifully I failed I would not get dis-

couraged, but instead I would try to uncover the cause of my anxiety and tension. In this manner I soon learned to master my weakness under the same conditions in which I had formerly failed. I enlisted the cooperation of my wife and two boys by asking them to help me make our home atmosphere one of peacefulness, tranquillity, harmony, and happiness. We talked in subdued voices, avoided loud and unnecessary noises, and we thought in terms of each other, not of ourselves. We have lived that way now for seven years, absorbing, radiating, sharing a happiness that we once knew nothing about.

I have tried to make clear the methods of direct approach with which I faced every new situation, offensively, and the manner in which I dealt with the personality traits which stood in my way in the presence of other persons. I depended upon actual experiences to fortify my confidence, for I knew that only in that way could I strengthen the conviction that I could talk, always, in the presence of anyone, under any conditions. I failed occasionally, and once I stuttered badly after I had been speaking without a falter for nearly a month, but by this time I had too many successful experiences behind me to be disturbed by one failure. I was satisfied that if I could make the correct adjustments within myself I would have no trouble with my adjustments to those about me.

The realization that I had finally won my battle and that the new personality of confidence and self-control, free from speech inhibitions, had become a reality, came to me after I had talked on the long distance telephone for seven minutes—four dollars and fifty cents—without the slightest feeling of hesitation. Then I knew that the idea, "I can", had become dominant in both the conscious and unconscious, and that smooth and fluent, effortless speech had been taken over by the unconscious habit regions of control.

CHAPTER NINE

Your Challenge

I HAD YET ONE IMPORTANT adjustment to make. Shortly before this significant victory over the telephone bugaboo occurred, I began to realize that in addition to the personality changes which had come about according to psychological laws and principles, a new force had unobtrusively come to life within me. It was during my periods of deepest relaxation that I was awakened to the fact that I was more than mind and body. Some call it a sixth or seventh sense; others prefer to ignore it. The poet, the artist, the musician, the father who realizes for the first time that the blood of his own veins is coursing through the body of a new-born child, even the true scientist, knows of this spiritual force but speaks of it guardedly as inspiration, or vision, or intuition. It seeks for expression within every one of us, but for the most part it lies dormant because we fear to entrust ourselves to that which we do not understand or cannot ex- plain. It came to me as a powerful urge to test further my capacities in new fields of endeavor, to delve deeper in silent quest of greater freedom and richer happiness. It directed my thoughts into serious meditation about a Supreme Being.

My childhood memories of the word "religion" brought to mind a hard, front row pew; a lusty, startling "Amen" from somewhere close behind me; a long, dusty drive home from church in a crowded buggy, and my father excusing the preacher for saying "hell" and "damnation", cluck- ing at the horse to punctuate his remarks. Worship always held for me the association of self-denial, of moaning chants, of a blind faith in some myster- ious benevolence that somehow failed to appear during the week. As a child I knew nothing of a friendly God. A long-faced, pious, old Sunday school teacher caused me to tremble in my belief of a watchful, punishing God whom I must fear and obey. Is it any wonder that I was willing to ac- cept a theory that denied the existence of such a supernatural tyrant?

I could not explain the new feeling of courage

and strength that was driving me to victory in whatever I attempted to do, nor could I keep from worrying about my inability to comprehend the simple faith which my children had in a divine protector. As it probably comes at one time or another in the lives of every one of us, the time had come for me to reach some satisfactory conclusion, so I set out to prove the nonexistence of a mysterious Creator. Is it necessary to tell you that I failed? I left Darwin in a jungle, playing hide-and-go-seek with the monkeys. I followed the theories of evolution until finally I flatly refused to believe that I was an animalized descendant of some scaly denizen of the sea. Was this world in the beginning a mere happen-so? It couldn't have been. Is the force of gravitation, that silent, powerful something which holds this universe together so perfectly, accidental? Nothing is accidental; there is a cause for everything. Do human beings wander aimlessly about on this earth with no more spiritual guidance than a dumb animal? We know better.

You may wonder what all this has to do with stuttering. A prominent psychiatrist told me personally that he always determined first of all if his patient had a belief in God. He said that there was no hope of curing a case of mental illness if the patient were an atheist, if there was nothing in his spiritual life to which he could cling with some de-

gree of security. And when I began trying to explain such phenomena as radio, electricity, hyp-
nosis, or insanity, I found that there was much going on about me in which I had absolute faith yet
could not understand.

I finally came to a very comforting decision.
Just as surely as my existence here, as a unit of a
great universal plan, is the fulfillment of a divine
Providence, so surely does my destiny lie in the
hands of a Supreme Being. It has been an inspiration and a great comfort to me—one that I missed
for thirty years while I lived in fear and distress—
to believe that I am never entirely alone in this
world. However, I do not believe that my future
course is in any way predestined. I have been
given intelligence, insight, and imagination — my
success or failure will be determined by the use
which I make of these capacities and by the extent
of the unfoldment of my spiritual self, which is the
greatest part of my endowment.

Men who have achieved in this world have been
guided by inspiration, by vision, by faith in themselves, and by faith in the unknown. Thomas
Edison never heard the true voice of a phonograph,
for he was deaf. He invented it in his imagination
and he died imagining, not knowing, that he had
created a phonograph which would reproduce
sound as we hear it. The plebeian limits himself

to those things which he can understand, and, therefore, he never achieves beyond the boundaries of recognized laws and facts. I refused to place limitations upon myself because I could not explain scientifically the forces which were at work within my spiritual self, lifting me above the anxieties which I had created with a distorted mind.

In case it is difficult for you to find a place for such a philosophy in your mental hygiene program, simply because for you its appeal is not logical or practical, let me ask you this question. Is stuttering practical? Has the scientist ever put his finger upon the definite cause or infallible cure? I can assure you that had I restricted myself to strictly scientific laws of cause and effect, had I created in my imagination no vision of this personality to be, and had I not been urged on by this powerful, inspired self which came to life when all practical effort seemed to be losing ground, I would never have accomplished the personality transformation which I made. And I would unquestionably count myself today among those psychologically inhibited personalities whom we speak of as stutterers.

My story is ended. My message to you is one of hope and encouragement. There is no reason why you cannot do what I have done, providing that you are psychologically ready to make the necessary readjustments and have faith in your ability to make them. My advice is to obtain as much knowledge as you possibly can, about your affliction, about your past, and about your present self. Apply this knowledge intelligently and begin living in the fullness of all of your capacities, intellectually and spiritually. Fit into your individual problem the principles which I have suggested to you directly, and those which you have read between the lines of my own life story. Make your application of them thorough and conscientious.

By thinking confidence, self-control, and calmness, and by acting with reserved composure as if you could not fail as you face every life situation, you will eventually establish these qualities as the genuine expressions of the new, rehabilitated personality. The freedom for which you are seeking and the happiness which comes with it will be found in the harmonious adjustments which you make towards all persons and conditions in your environment, but it will not come from the outside to you. It must radiate from a nucleus of perfect harmony within, a condition that can exist only with emotional control and a state of mind that is free from imaginary limitations.

BIBLIOGRAPHY

THOUGHT CONTROL IN EVERYDAY LIFE
by James Alexander
(Presents daily life adjustments and how to make them)

THE NATURE AND TREATMENT OF STAMMERING
by Boome and Richardson
(Treatment through relaxation, as practiced in London clinics)

SECRET SPRINGS   *by Harvey O'Higgins*
(A fascinating presentation of conflicts and their solution)

FOR STUTTERERS   *by Blanton and Blanton*
(Late presentation of stammering as emotional)

UNDERSTANDING HUMAN NATURE   *by Alfred Adler*
(Stresses inferiority complex as basis of all conflict)

SPEECH DEFECTS AND THEIR CORRECTION
by Mabel F. Gifford
(Pamphlet used by California teachers of speech correction, includes causes of stuttering and fluency image of speech)

PERSONALITY, ITS DEVELOPMENT AND HYGIENE
by Dr. Winifred Richmond
(A study of personality types, maladjustments, and helpful hygiene)

OUTWITTING OUR NERVES   *by Josephine Jackson*
(Nervous disorders and their correction through adjustment)

SUGGESTION AND AUTOSUGGESTION
by Charles Baudouin
(Presents the practical application of autosuggestion)

WAKE UP AND LIVE!   *by Dorothea Brande*
(A helpful mental hygiene program for stutterers)

A FORTUNE TO SHARE   *by Vash Young*
(Popular treatise on nervous disorders, fear, inferiority, and other weaknesses, and their elimination through mental hygiene)

ABOUT OURSELVES   *by H. A. Overstreet*
(A practical study of human behavior and problems of adjustment)

$1.75

MY PERSONAL acquaintance with the author, Mr. Wedberg, extending over a period of twenty years, includes the college experiences of which he writes so vividly in this book. At that time he was one of the most severe stutterers I have ever known. Since his emancipation from this speech handicap I have been associated with him as a successful playwright, dramatic producer, actor, and fluent speaker.

Further it has been my privilege to read the original manuscript of this book, which in my opinion is a forceful inspiration to anyone afflicted with this psychological speech disorder.

PROF. E. R. NICHOLS,

Head of the Speech Department, University of Redlands.